COLDSPRING:
THE TRIAL

COLDSPRING: THE TRIAL

CHERI MANCUSO AND JOHN SCARANO

DANCING MOON PRESS
NEWPORT. OREGON

ISBN-13: 978-1-892076-79-3
Library of Congress Control Number: 2010937554
Mancuso, Cheri, and Scarano, John
Coldspring: The Trial
1. Title; 2. Coldspring, New York; 3. Cattaraugus County, New York; 4. Cattaraugus Hills; 5. Southern Tier, New York; 6. Bernice Kenyon Farnsworth; 7. Harold Farnsworth; 8. Alfred "Freddy" Joseph Lindsay; 9. Lewis E. Lawes; 10. Amos O. Squire; 11. Sing Sing Correctional Facility; 12. "Old Sparky"; 13. Electrocution of criminals; 14. Death penalty; 15. Capital punishment; 16. True crime; 17. Karma

Manufactured in the United States of America
Front cover photo of "Old Sparky" courtesy of Ossining Historical
    Society
Author photo courtesy of Jack Berger, East Randolph, N.Y.
Cover production by Jennifer Blessing Gerbino
Book design by Carla Perry, Dancing Moon Press

DANCING MOON PRESS
P.O. Box 832, Newport, OR 97365
541-574-7708
www.dancingmoonpress.com
info@dancingmoonpress.com

FIRST EDITION

ACKNOWLEDGMENTS

J. Michael Shane, son of G. Sydney Shane
Jo Short, daughter-in-law of Helen Short
Jolynn Benn
Marlynn Olson
Leone Pickup, Jr.
E. J. Shiflet, daughter of Leone Pickup, Jr.
Dean Waite
Annette Waite
Jeanne Woodruff-Blessing
Jennifer Blessing-Gerbino, graphic artist
Ted Searle, "Teddy" in this book
Nina Meyers, wife of Fred Meyers in this book
Tyler Searle
Sheila Searle
Kathy Krieger Searle, niece of Colonel A. Edward Krieger
Jane Arrance
Tim Arrance
Mrs. Paul Arrance
Joe Bialecki, current owner of the McGraw Farm property
Kristine Bialecki, daughter of Joe Bialecki
Harold Williams, the jeweler in this book
Catherine McLarney
Hobie Wagner
Diana Mackey, Randolph Historical Society
Sharon Fellowes, Cattaraugus County Historical Museum and
    Research Center
Cattaraugus County Sheriff's Department
James K. Griffth, Cattaraugus County Clerk
Sandra Wogick, former Cattaraugus County Clerk
Cindy Collins, Publicist
Deborah Everts, Salamanca Press

Olean Times-Herald
Randolph Register
Jamestown Post-Journal
Buffalo News
Buffalo and Erie County Library
Norman T. MacDonald, President, Ossining Historical Society
Adam A. Wolpinsky, photo archivist, Ossining Historical Society
Arthur M. Wolpinsky, photographer & historian, Sing Sing Prison
Phillip Heath, Superintendent, Sing Sing Prison
Lewis E. Lawes, former Sing Sing Prison Warden, Author of *20,000 Years in Sing Sing*
Amos O. Squire, former Sing Sing Chief Physician, Author of *Sing Sing Doctor*

DEDICATION

This book is dedicated to J. Michael Shane, Esq., the son of
G. Sydney Shane. Without his valuable input and assistance in
obtaining the Grand Jury and Trial testimony for Alfred J.
Lindsay, this story could not have been told with such great detail
and accuracy.

FOREWORD

In the first book of the *Coldspring* series, the reincarnation of two men and one woman is chronicled from Ice Age Siberia all the way onto and across the North American Continent to the Farnsworth's farm in Coldspring, New York, circa 1935. We experienced the mutation of their roles in several of their lifetimes together and observed their futile attempts to resolve their karmic debt to one another. It required thousands of years for their shared karma to explode into violence at a place named Coldspring. When the initial violence occurs, the hapless trio is compelled to return to that place to die two more times.

In this second volume, *Coldspring: The Trial,* we return to the town of Coldspring after the double-murder and now, the trio's only hope for karmic resolution depends entirely on the one member who remains alive in the physical realm. That man is Alfred "Freddy" Lindsay and as the book opens, he is on the run after murdering Bernice and Harry Farnsworth. Freddy is driving Bernice's 1930 Chevrolet Sport Coupe.

The remainder of Freddy's time on earth is limited and so is his opportunity to break the chain of violence that binds his soul to the souls of Bernice and Harry.

As this story of love, murder, shared karma and redemption continues to unfold, Cattaraugus County, New York, in 1935 comes back to life. We get a taste of what it was like to live in that time period through the parade of characters that were involved in Freddy's trial for first degree murder. And the trial is definitely a telling look at American Justice in that era.

Near the end of this volume, Freddy Lindsay makes a discovery that has the potential to set the trio on a new karmic path. Will this new path lead them away from the violence in which they've been locked? That question will be answered in the third book in this series, *Coldspring: The Resolution.*

Years of research and good solid detective work has gone into this book. Every effort has been made to ensure that the story unfolds in much the same manner as the events took place seventy-five years ago. This was made possible by the acquisition of the Grand Jury testimony from March 1935 and the Lindsay Trial transcript, which was found attached to Freddy's appeal records stored in Rochester, New York. Both documents were obtained by J. Michael Shane and we will always remain in debt to him for his assistance.

We also relied heavily on the published works of former Sing Sing Warden Lewis E. Lawes and former Chief Physician Amos O. Squire. Both men described the execution process and the horrific effects of electrocution on the human body from their eye-witness accounts. They also described Freddy Lindsay's experiences after he arrived at the death house in Sing Sing Correctional Facility. Lawes and Squire officiated at more than one hundred and fifty executions each before their retirement. Squire retired because the trauma of witnessing so many deaths filled him with an obsession that nearly caused him to touch the bodies of the condemned as they were being electrocuted.

In addition, we received a plethora of historical photos and information from the Ossining Historical Society. Sing Sing is located in the town of Ossining, New York.

In this book we included a graphic description of Freddy's execution but it is not offered to sensationalize his death. Rather, we present it here as a reminder to never return to electrocution as a method of "humane" execution. And, because many innocent people have gone to their death in an execution chamber, reading of Freddy's execution may compel you to oppose the death penalty here in the United States when given the chance to voice your opinion. In either case, the electrocution process as it is described in this book is meant to be provocative. We leave the issues that revolve around legal execution for others to decide.

—John Scarano, 2010

CHAPTER ONE

A DIMINUTIVE BLACK AND WHITE CHICKADEE CLUTCHED A THIN branch in its feet at the top of a large Maple tree that faced the McGraw farmhouse in Coldspring, New York. The tiny bird raised its small black-capped head, opened its beak and sang out its singsong call into the frigid, late morning air on March 5, 1935. It seemed to call out the two-syllable name of the woman who faithfully scattered black oil Sunflower seeds shortly before lunchtime each day onto the farmhouse's front porch for all the resident birds, chipmunks and squirrels. This particular Chickadee's limited rendition of "Bern-ice, Bern-ice" rang out loudly several times in the dry, cold winter air. As it sang, the Chickadee could not have known that its calls would prove fruitless. Nor could it have known that Bernice Kenyon Farnsworth, who seemed to be the object of its call, lay dead on her back with her head askew on the cold, hard-packed dirt floor of the farmhouse cellar. The bird was also oblivious that her husband, Harry Farnsworth, also lay dead on his back, positioned almost exactly above her on the first floor of the two-story building. A simple and brief flight to the dining room or cellar windows could have easily confirmed each of those facts. But, the little Chickadee was not inclined to abandon its perch and so the bodies continued to lay in their respective locations, unmoved, unseen, and unknown to the rural world that lay just beyond their stiffened bodies.

The interior temperature of the farmhouse had already begun to chill, as its inhabitants had not tended the fires that usually kept it warm. In the foyer between the dining room and the sitting

1

room, a small pool of dark coagulating blood had formed under Harry's head. The floorboards beneath his head were old and had shrunken considerably over the years, creating small gaps between each board. Harry's blood seeped slowly through these gaps and dripped slowly into the cellar below.

Bernice's body lay directly below in the basement. Her head was crowned by a blood-soaked crescent of dirt. Occasionally, one thick drop of Harry's blood hit the moist dirt bloodstain with a dull thud. It was the only sound that broke the silence in the cellar. Eventually, Harry's blood thickened as the temperature continued to drop upstairs. Soon the dripping of his blood stopped altogether. The cellar became as silent as a burial tomb.

Meanwhile, Bernice's 1930 Chevy Sport Coupe was motoring down Highway 17 towards Olean, New York, at a very fast clip. Sitting behind the wheel was her murderer, Alfred "Freddy" Lindsay. Freddy was hunched over, gripping the wheel so tightly that his fingers lost blood circulation and turned white. He muttered to himself, trying desperately to come up with a plan of action. So large was his fright that he was unable to think coherently. His mind was obsessed with visions of the electric chair at Sing Sing Prison.

Freddy knew all too well about the famous electric chair known as "Old Sparky." He had become familiar with it, as all inmates do, when he'd been incarcerated at Sing Sing. Memories of the lockdowns that took place each time Old Sparky was fired up for an execution flooded back to him. The executions served to remind each prisoner of his own mortality and for a few hours they would become agitated, imagining the horror of watching the last few minutes of their lives count down on a clock on Death Row.

Eventually, Freddy realized he was now eligible to join the ranks of those condemned men and women. And he knew he could experience that same countdown moment firsthand. This realization filled him with panic. He rocked back and forth as he drove, crying hysterically as he guided the car into a tunnel of shade from large Maple trees growing on both sides of the highway.

The car's presence set off calamity in a flock of black crows that resided in the tangled mass of tree branches that formed the upper walls of the tunnel. They instantly took to the sky, cawing loudly into the gray sky. They circled the stand of Maple trees waiting for the car to emerge on the far end so they could reclaim their domain. From afar, it might have appeared to the untrained eye that the Maple stand was besieged by a flock of vultures poised to descend upon their prey after the first sign of its death.

Inside the tree-lined tunnel Freddy's panic increased two-fold. In his manic state he imagined that the long thin maple branches above him were elongated human arms with outstretched claw-like hands intent upon locking him in their powerful clutches. Luckily for him the car shot out of the tunnel before the terror rising in his gut caused him to lose complete control of the car.

When the gray winter daylight relit the interior of the car, a huge wave of relief washed over him. But the calm did not last long. Freddy replayed the image of the outstretched hands in the tunnel and was transformed. He was no longer Freddy Lindsay, petty criminal. He became Freddy Lindsay, desperate double-murderer. He cast furtive glances to the front, side and back of the car. He could feel the hot breath of his pursuers on the back of his neck, imagining them bearing down on him.

Freddy continued to drive on East Highway 17 toward the town of Salamanca. The shock of what he had done prevented him from focusing on the predicament that lay ahead. Eventually, normal thought processes returned and he realized the need for a plan of action. However, no real plan came to him. Instead, he headed for New York City and the town of New Rochelle that lay nearby. He figured that once he arrived in the City, he would figure things out.

Freddy remained hunched over the wheel of the car and drove on for more than an hour and a half without shifting his position—as if he were creating the forward momentum of the car through sheer will. He motored obliviously through the towns of Salamanca, Allegheny, and Olean. Just as he approached the outskirts of the town of Cuba, the Sport Coupe sputtered and lost power. Glancing down, Freddy realized the needle on the gas gauge rested on empty. He guided the car to the side of the road and let it come to rest. He leaned back into the seat and placed his hands on top of his head. He let out a big breath and then cursed himself aloud for being so stupid as to let the car run out of gas.

Freddy continued to sit in the driver's seat as he stared blankly at the H&R pistol that lay on the passenger seat next to him. Once again, he castigated himself audibly for such stupidity. He grabbed the pistol and exited the car. He looked up and down the highway to make sure there were no witnesses. Satisfied that he was alone, he walked around the front of the car and tossed the pistol far into the field alongside the road. Murderer or not, Freddy had no use for the weapon. And he didn't need anything around that reminded him of what he had done back at the farmhouse earlier that morning.

He returned to the driver's side of the car, shifted it out of gear, and began pushing it down the highway towards Cuba. He prayed that no car would approach him from either direction, and if anyone stopped, that they would not offer assistance. He was also worried about interacting with the attendant at the gas station he hoped to find. For the first time that day, Freddy was lucky. A gas station was located a mile and a half from where he had run out of gas.

As Freddy approached, a gas station attendant ran up to the moving car. The attendant helped Freddy push the car off the road and park it next to a gravity-style gas pump in front of an old, weathered wooden garage. Freddy avoided conversation and answered the inquisitive attendant's questions with one lie after another. He paid the attendant a dollar and a half for eleven gallons of Ethyl gasoline and prepared to leave as soon as he fired up the car's engine. Just as he shifted the car into first gear, he glanced to his right and scanned a road sign listing distances to nearby towns. New York City lay 330 miles ahead. He let out the clutch and motored forward.

Freddy drove on, mile after mile, toward New York City. He stopped only once to purchase a sandwich and a cup of coffee in Binghamton, New York. He drove straight through until he reached a ferry off River Road in Edgewater, New Jersey, at ten o'clock that evening. He steered the Coupe up an old wooden dock and onto a multi-windowed ferry that crossed the Hudson River. When the ferry docked at 125th Street in New York City, he drove the Coupe off onto another wooden dock and made his way down to the street. He spotted a bar and parked the Coupe near it. He went into the bar, located a phone booth, and sat down inside it.

An old girlfriend lived in Manhattan. She had been Freddy's only true girlfriend and he had frequently corresponded with her after his arrest in 1927 for third degree burglary. He'd often confessed his love for her in his letters and for a long while she did the same. But slowly, over time, her letters diminished in frequency. By late 1929, while he was still incarcerated at Sing Sing Prison, she wrote a final letter to him explaining that she had fallen in love with another man and married him. Freddy's response was to wallow in self-pity and self-hate. Over the ensuing years he berated himself whenever he thought about her. Now, however, the memory of Madeline Glossheir stirred up a longing inside his gut. Suddenly he needed to see her, to speak with her and to touch her one more time. He felt an internal death

5

clock ticking deep within. He knew beyond the shadow of a doubt that he was going to die and that it would be sooner rather than later.

Freddy cradled the earpiece in his neck as he opened the wallet-softened paper with Madeline's phone number and address. He hesitated briefly before placing the call to her. He begged some unseen agent that Madeline would answer the phone instead of her husband. The phone rang several times before a woman's sleepy voice answered. Freddy's heart almost leapt out of his chest at the sound of her voice.

"Madeline," he said excitedly, "this is Freddy, Freddy Lindsay."

"Oh my gosh, Freddy. I can't believe it!" she replied, "I haven't heard from you in years! Where are you calling from? And why are you calling so late? We were in bed."

"I know it's late, but I just got into town and I'm not going to be here long. I really want to see you tonight, Madeline. It's very important. I wouldn't ask if it wasn't. You know that, don't you?"

"Right now? Tonight? You want to see me tonight, Freddy?"

"Yes, tonight, Madeline. I know it's crazy, but I may not be able to see you again for a long time. Five minutes, Madeline. That's all I ask. Five minutes. Whaddya say? Can I come up right now? I'm only a couple of minutes away from you."

"Oh, geez, Freddy. I don't know. George is asleep in the bedroom but he'd kill me if he caught me downstairs talking to you in the middle of the night."

"Five minutes, Madeline. He'll sleep for those five minutes, easy. Meet me in front of your building. I'm on my way."

Freddy hung up the phone and dashed out of the booth and exited the bar. He ran to the Coupe and started it up. He headed further down 125th Street and turned right onto Riverside Drive. He continued down Riverside Drive until he came to 104th Street, where he turned left. When he passed Madeline's apartment building he parked the Coupe curbside and walked back to her building. He scanned upwards and spotted a woman's figure on a second floor fire escape landing. As soon as Madeline saw him she waved her arms. He waved back and she motioned that she would meet him downstairs.

Freddy waited at a wooden door with the number 208 etched into a single pane of glass. He stepped back and gazed intently at her as she came through the door towards him. She was dressed in a heavy terrycloth night robe and her hair was bed-rumpled. Freddy thought she looked fantastic.

Madeline looked across and up and down the street before she threw her arms around him and gave him a long hug. Freddy caught the scent of her hair and a thrill ran through him. He silently vowed to remember this moment forever.

"What's going on, Freddy? You're in trouble again, aren't you? I can always tell, you know! So don't lie to good old Madeline 'cause it won't work."

"Yes, I am in trouble, but I don't want to talk about it. It's not important right now. What is important now is that I've seen you and that I've talked to you. That's all. Just that, Madeline. My god, it's good to see you!"

He started to reach his right hand up to stroke her hair but she flinched backwards to avoid contact.

"Freddy, don't. You know I'm married and there's no way you and I will ever have again what we had before. That's life in the big city, right Freddy? No regrets and just good memories. That's how I always remember you, Freddy. I remember you with good memories."

"Yeah, Madeline, just good memories. I got it."

Freddy paused for a moment and they both felt awkward in the ensuing silence. A few moments later he spoke again and raised his right hand. "Remember this tattoo on my hand? Whenever I look at it I remember the first time I showed it to you.

Do you remember that? And you cried because you understood that the words 'True Love' were meant for you? Whenever I look at it, I remember that and all of the rest of our good memories. Thanks for seeing me, Madeline. I gotta go. I gotta see my sister, Helen, in New Rochelle before I move on. Have a great life, Madeline. You deserve it."

"You're scaring me now, Freddy. You sound like you're saying goodbye forever. What have you done? Surely, you can tell me."

"You'll find out in good time, Madeline. When you do, remember me as Freddy from Port Chester, New York. Remember me as the guy next door who you fell in love with. And try to forgive me. If the cops come looking for me, tell them you haven't heard from me in years. I won't mention that I saw you either. No sense draggin' you into my mess. Bye, Madeline."

"Bye, Freddy. You'll always occupy a special place in my heart. Stay in touch with me if you can."

"Sure. Sure, I will."

Madeline watched Freddy turn away and walk to his car. She sighed as he drove away into the night and wondered for the thousandth time what her life might have been if things had gone differently for Freddy and her. She also wondered what Freddy had done that might cause the police to come looking for him. She softly retraced her steps leading to her second floor apartment.

A sense of dread filled Freddy as he left Madeline standing at the doorstep of her apartment building. The realization that he would never see her again was powerful. He became acutely aware of his mortality in a new way—his execution date lay straight ahead of him; that was clear. This renewed awareness filled him with a panic that almost made him scream out in anguish. He pushed the unwanted feeling down into his gut like he always did, but this time the pain wouldn't lie dormant. It began to corrode the fiber of Freddy's nerve, which gradually paralyzed him.

Freddy shifted his focus to heading for New Rochelle immediately. He knew he could turn to his sister, Helen, in a pinch. With fresh motivation, he drove down 104th Street to Amsterdam Avenue and turned left. He drove up to 110th Street and turned right. Just before he reached Columbus Avenue, the Coupe began to sputter and hesitate just as it had done earlier that day in Cuba. Freddy looked down at the gas gauge and groaned. He'd run out of gas again and this time there was no way to get the car to a gas station. He coasted around the corner onto Columbus Avenue. He brought the car to a stop at 983 Columbus Avenue. Panic rose again like mercury on a hot summer day. When it reached its peak, every nerve in his body was stimulated. Unable to control himself, he deliberately, slowly shut down until he felt numb. In that state of mind, he abandoned the car and his small bundle of clothing, and began walking.

After a long while, Freddy came to an entrance of the Elevated train, boarded, made his way to the last car and sat down. He rode the El back and forth for the remainder of the night. Sometimes, sleep came to him but it was always interrupted by nightmares of the murders of Bernice and Harry. He sat hunched over as he contemplated his life and his fate.

His thoughts drifted through his childhood as the train clacked monotonously down the steel El tracks. Freddy delineated his life by the occurrence of tragic events. Life up to the time of his father's death was a murky fog. In contrast, his father's death remained crystalline in his memory. That was when things began to go badly for him and his family. Freddy reminisced about the life of petty crime that he and his brother, Bob, undertook to support his family. Memories of time spent in reform schools flooded past him like a movie. It was in a reform school that he chose to become a criminal for life. Jail time began after he was eighteen and he graduated to prison time in Sing Sing by the time he turned twenty-one. An image of his mother floated up in his mind. She was sitting in a courtroom behind him, her eyes flooded with tears as the judge pronounced sentence on him. The helplessness he felt that day filled him again and he cursed himself once more for disappointing her. In time, he recalled how he had come to Harry and Bernice's farm on that frigid December day.

Freddy remembered how cold Bernice was toward him at first and when he overheard Bernice and Harry argue about whether or not Freddy should stay. He recalled the times that Bernice refused to let him accompany Harry in the car and her words stung him again. He thought about the fistfight when he soundly beat Harry and the scene played out in his mind. He could hear Bernice's haughty voice telling him she was royalty, which implied he was nothing. Freddy's cheeks burned hot with anger and shame as he heard her voice repeat the words over and over.

His mind wandered back to a memory that surprised him: the tenderness that Bernice and Harry shared in brief encounters around the farmhouse and in the barn. Sometimes it was a little kiss on the lips, and other times they communicated their love for one another in a glance or during a shared laugh. Bernice would put her hand on Harry and with a small, tender smile she would convey 'I love you.' Freddy's jealousy rose in him again. It made him squirm and he paced in the train trying to focus on anything else but the love between Bernice and Harry. He knew where his walk down memory lane was leading him—right back down into the basement of the Farnsworth house. Freddy did not want to go there ever again. He did not want to remember the heinous act of violence he had committed in that dank, musty, subterranean room. He pushed away the memory of the farmhouse and focused instead on his favorite pastime—feeling sorry for himself.

By the time the oppressive darkness of night mercifully gave way to daylight, Freddy came to a decision. Being a natural pessimist and possessing a very weak will, he decided it was futile to try and escape his fate. He committed himself to do nothing, to let the chips fall as they may.

Freddy left the El and began to wander aimlessly in Manhattan. A growing awareness of hunger caused him to enter a small restaurant where he ordered a meager breakfast. A man sitting on the counter stool next to him struck up a conversation. When Freddy disclosed his homelessness, the man invited Freddy to come up and stay with him in his room located in a nearby flophouse. Freddy agreed and left with the man. Once they arrived at the sleazy hotel, it quickly became apparent that the man was interested in a sexual liaison. When the man excused himself to use the communal hallway bathroom, Freddy walked out. He wondered what was in him that attracted people who did not respect him. It seemed to be a reoccurring pattern. His depression dropped to its lowest level.

Once again, Freddy headed for the El train line and the solace of the rear car. He spent the rest of the day riding back and forth, oblivious to the commuters who joined him in a haphazard progression. He was unaware that oncoming passengers avoided sitting next to him. Some of them even turned around and exited the car upon seeing him brooding in his seat. They could feel the negative vibrations that Freddy unconsciously projected and were instinctively afraid of him. Freddy remained on the train for the entire day and night of Wednesday, March 6.

When dawn broke on Thursday morning, Freddy exited the El, ate breakfast and wandered the City. On a whim, he entered Central Park and sat on a bench where he remained for hours brooding over his situation. He considered turning himself in to the police. Then, once he made up his mind to do it, he rose from the park bench in search of a police station. His wanderings led him to the steps of a precinct station and he gazed at the glass doors that framed the entrance. Try as he might, he could not get his right foot to lift and place itself on the first step that led to the door. He was frozen in place by fear.

When one of the doors opened and a man exited the building, it broke the spell. Freddy turned and walked away at a feigned normal pace. His heart raced wildly and his pulse pounded visibly in one of his jugular veins as he imagined a policeman bearing down on him. His breathing calmed after a few uneventful blocks and he began searching again for another entrance to the El train. Surrender to the police was not an option.

Again, Freddy took advantage of the safe haven that the El provided for him. He rode the train until dawn on Friday morning, March 8, 1935. He exited the station and noticed his clothing was becoming soiled and his body odor was quite strong. He decided that a visit to his sister, Helen, was in order. Perhaps, he reasoned, he could bathe, get a good night's sleep and a change of clothing. He set out hitchhiking for New Rochelle immediately after breakfast. He caught his first ride from a delivery truck driver in upper Manhattan and left New York City at around nine o'clock in the morning.

CHAPTER TWO

FRESH, CRYSTALLINE-WHITE SNOW LAY ON THE GROUND IN Coldspring, New York on the morning of Friday, March 8, 1935. It had fallen steadily the previous night. William W. Whitmore, a farmhand, shivered and drew his collar up to shield his bare neck from an errant cold breeze as he crossed the barnyard to answer a call from his employer, Ira Newton Bennett. William's tall, lanky figure cast a stark shadow on the snow-covered ground and it followed him up onto the mudroom at the back of the Bennett farmhouse. Ira, a 64-year-old farmer, stood waiting for William behind the glass-paned mudroom door. He opened the door for William as he climbed the steps to the porch.

"You finished mucking the horse stalls, William?" Ira asked his hired hand.

"Yes, Ira. I was just about ready to head up to the hay mow when you called out for me," William said in a deliberate manner.

"Well, forget that for now, boy. I got somethin' else for ya to do. Is that wood rack still leaning up against the barn on the North side?"

"Yes, sir, it is. Are you wanting to send it on over to the Farnsworth farm this morning?"

"Yes, as a matter of fact, that is exactly why I called you up from the barn. Farnsworth was here the other day asking to take it back. I expected him to fetch it now that it has snowed. I figure he must be ready for it as he was nigh ready to finish cutting up the logs in his woods on Monday. Let's hitch up a horse to the sleigh and I'll help you load 'er up. You can tend to the hay when you get back."

Ira finished buttoning his winter coat, slipped his hands into his mittens, and led William out to the barn. They hitched a horse to the sleigh and then lifted the wood rack onto it. Satisfied that the rack was securely resting on the sleigh, Ira returned to the house and William drove down the snow-covered dirt driveway and turned left onto Price's Corners Road. Minutes later he passed through the undergrade at the end of the road and made his way to the Farnsworth farm just a short distance up McGraw Road. Once there, William headed up the short driveway that led to the farmhouse and barn. He pulled up on the reins and brought the horse and sleigh to a stop.

William Whitmore, 32 years old, was what some people might call a 'deep thinker.' He drove most people to distraction because he had a bad habit of stopping in mid-sentence in order to think of what else he had to say. William sat and contemplated the scene that lay before him in much the same manner. *Something is wrong here*, he thought. He began to tick off the incongruities of the scene that lay before him. There were no tracks in the fresh snow leading back and forth across the barnyard. Bernice's Coupe was not in its usual spot between the house and the barn. There were no tire tracks indicating the car had been there since last night.

He jerked his head towards the barn as he became aware of an awful racket coming from inside it. He noted that the snow had not been cleared from the swinging path of the large barn door. William slapped the reins in his hands against the horse's back and it lurched forward. He guided the horse up to the north side of the barn and brought the horse and sleigh to a stop.

William tipped the wood rack off of the sleigh and leaned it up against the silo attached to the barn. Having accomplished that task, he decided to see if anyone was inside the barn.

As he swung open the barn door the sight shocked him. Several calves were lying on the filthy floor. Even though the light was dim, he could see they were breathing heavily. The cows in the barn were tearing at the stanchions to which they were tethered, and the horses had become pinned in the manger. William called out loudly to see if anyone was in the barn, but received no answer. Not knowing what to do next he closed the barn door and immediately headed back to Ira's farm.

Once William was back at Ira Bennett's property, he entered the farmhouse through the mudroom and came upon Ira sipping on a cup of coffee in the kitchen. Ira gave William a quizzical look as it was very unusual for his hired hand to enter the house without first knocking.

"What's gotten into you, William? Have ya lost your manners, boy?" he asked gruffly.

"Somethin' isn't right up to the Farnsworth place, Ira. Somethin' isn't right at all!" William replied.

"What are you talkin' about, boy? What isn't right?"

"I went up like you said and dropped the wood rack off at the Farnsworth barn and I heard the animals bawlin' to beat all. And there wasn't no tracks in the snow either. That isn't right, Ira. There shoulda been tracks going back and forth from the house to the barn by this time of day, don't ya think?"

"Yeah, there oughta be a lot by this time of day, all right. Did you go up to the house and check on the Farnsworths?"

"No, sir, I did not. I went into the barn and hollered out a hello and there wasn't nobody there to answer me. The animals look like they haven't been tended to for a couple of days. The calves were dry and heavin' and the cows were tearing at their stanchions. I got out of there quick. Somethin' isn't right at all, I tell ya. Not right at all."

Ira stroked his chin between his thumb and forefinger while he thought over the situation.

"No, it doesn't sound right at all. That wouldn't be like Farnsworth to ignore his stock like that. The two of them could have gotten stuck in Salamanca last night in the snowstorm. I tell you what, it's close to noon, so why don't you head on home for dinner and stop off at the Farnsworths' place on your way back? If you don't find any fresh tracks there, you come on back here and I'll go up to their place with you."

William nodded his head in agreement and left the kitchen to have dinner with his wife, Ethel. He returned at one o'clock and informed Ira that there were no fresh tracks in the snow when he went back to the Farnsworth's farm. But Ira was not too eager to butt in on anybody's business and hesitated to go out to the Farnsworth farm.

Grace McCabe Bennett, Ira's wife, prodded him to go up and take care of the animals. "It's the neighborly thing to do, Ira! And think of those poor animals. It sounds like they haven't been watered or fed for several days."

Convinced by Grace's argument, Ira went out to the barn where he and William saddled up two horses. They left immediately for the Farnsworth farm on McGraw Road. They arrived without incident and dismounted their horses near the rear of the farmhouse.

"Hmm," Ira mused, "looks too quiet to me, too, boy. Let's go in through the mudroom in back and see what's up, eh?"

"I'm not goin' in there, Ira. I'm tellin' ya somethin's wrong in there. I can just feel it."

"Now, now, boy, don't get yourself all worked up over nothin'. You're spooking yourself, that's all. Now come on, let's go in. It's colder than a witch's tit out here."

Nothing Ira said convinced William to enter the house. Ira finally shrugged his shoulders and said, "Okay, boy. Have it your way. Keep watch on the horses until I get back."

Ira stepped up to the mudroom door that sat askew from the doorframe. Snow had blown in and piled up on the floor inside. He could see that the back door to the kitchen was also standing open about eighteen inches. William's intuition was beginning to carry some weight. *Why would anyone leave his door open on such a cold winter day?* Ira thought as he opened the door and entered the small kitchen. The small table inside was neatly set for two and there were two pots sitting on flameless burners on top of the kerosene cooking stove. The kitchen was ice cold, indicating that it had been left unheated for quite some time. Not wanting to barge in on the Farnsworths if they were indeed home, Ira called out, "Yoo-hoo! Anyone home? Yoo-hoo!"

His loud voiced echoed in kitchen. It did not elicit a response. Convinced that there was no one home, Ira ventured into the dimly lit dining room. Then he crossed over towards the sitting room where he discovered Harry's body laid out by the front door near the stairway leading to the second floor. Ira let out a loud whistle as he removed his mittens. He gingerly laid his hand on one of Harry's cold hands just to make sure the man was dead.

Thoughts raced through his mind: *Where is Bernice? And where's their hired hand?*

Ira stepped over Harry's legs and made for the stairs. He went up to the second floor where he inspected each of the four bedrooms. Every room was in shambles. Dresser drawers had been pulled out and ransacked. Their contents lay strewn on the floors of each room. Satisfied that Bernice was not upstairs, Ira went back down to the first floor, stepped over Harry again and made his way to the buttery door. He opened it and discovered that it led back into the kitchen. He turned around and saw the cellar door slightly ajar. He took a deep breath and made his way down the cellar stairs. He stopped abruptly near the bottom when he caught his first glimpse of Bernice lying on the dirt floor. When he stepped close enough to determine that she was dead, he headed back up the stairs and entered the kitchen through the buttery door. Once outside he gave William the bad news.

"I don't know how you knew it, boy, but you were right. Things aren't right at all here, that's for sure! The Farnsworth's have both been murdered!" he exclaimed.

The news had a devastating effect on William. He began to shiver and begged Ira to let him leave.

"No, boy. You got to go in with me and be a witness. Now buck up and get yourself in there!" Ira shoved William towards the mudroom door. "We'll head out for a phone when we're done here. I'll call Deputy Sheriff Leone Pickup at his house in Randolph and get him up here right away."

Ira had to keep pushing William through the house and down into the basement. When William saw Bernice's body, he burst into tears and ran back up the stairs screaming. He did not stop until he reached the horses tethered to the lightning rod grounding post half-buried in earth next to the house.

"You ought not to have done that to me, Ira," he wailed. "Mrs. Farnsworth treated me real good when I was stayin' and workin' here. I'll see her lying there with her head cut off every night when I go to bed and close my eyes! You ought not to have done that to me!"

"Oh, stop your snivelin' now! It's over with and there's no need for you to go down there again. Let's get on down to Ruell Wheeler's place. He's got a phone. You just remember what we saw, boy. I don't want anyone thinking that we had anything to do with this. You got that, William?"

"Yes, sir. I got it. I still say you ought not to have done that to me, Ira." William was sullen as he wiped the mucous away from his nose with the back of his hand.

Ira rolled his eyes back. "Oh, brother, William! Come on, let's go!"

They mounted their horses and made off for Ruell Wheeler's house. When they got there and gave Ruell the news, he reeled back in shock. Ira went into Ruell's kitchen, fumbled through his wallet looking for Leone Pickup's phone number, and rang up the Pickup household. Ira spoke quietly to someone on the other end and then hung the earpiece back on its cradle. He walked to Ruell's sitting room where William and Ruell were discussing what William had seen at the Farnsworth home.

"Thanks for the use of the phone, Ruell," said Ira. "Deputy Pickup wasn't there but his wife, Ella, said she'd find him and send him on up to the Farnsworth place. She was pretty shook up at the news. Seems she knew Bernice pretty well. Let's go, William. We need to be there when Leone comes up."

Once Ira and William were gone, Ruell Wheeler wasted no time. He called everyone he knew to tell them about Bernice and Harold's murder. Within thirty minutes, the news had spread throughout Cattaraugus County.

Ira and William returned to the Farnsworth farm and tended to the livestock in the barn while they waited for Deputy Sheriff Pickup to arrive. Despite their valiant effort, the calves were beyond saving. They died quietly, one after another, long before Pickup arrived with State Trooper Lieutenant William J. George at three o'clock. Lieutenant George was the commanding officer at the State Trooper Outpost in Friendship, New York. They arrived on foot after leaving Lieutenant George's car at the entrance to McGraw Road to avoid getting stuck in the deep snow.

Deputy Sheriff Pickup and Lieutenant George saw that the barn door stood open and assumed Ira was inside taking care of the livestock, so they headed in that direction. The condition of the barn's interior and the abysmal state of the livestock surprised them. Ira looked up at the two men as they entered the barn and greeted his good friend.

"Say, Leone!" said Ira, "it's good to see you even under these conditions!"

"And just what are 'these conditions,' Ira?" Deputy Sheriff Leone asked as he shook Ira's outstretched hand.

Ira hesitated as he looked over at Lieutenant George, whom he did not know.

"This is Lieutenant George. He's the commanding officer at the Friendship State Troopers Post. He was with me when I got the call from my wife. He's here to help with the initial investigation," explained Pickup. "Lieutenant George, this is Ira Bennett, a farmer. And over there, tending to the horses is William Whitmore. Hey, William, good to see ya!"

William looked up and acknowledged Pickup with a short head nod then went back to work on the horses in the manger.

"Pleased to meet ya, Lieutenant George," Ira said as he shook the Lieutenant's hand. "I guess it's best for you to see for yourself, Leone. Let's go up to the house. William, you stay here and keep workin' on the stock."

William was visibly relieved that he was not asked to re-enter the house. He nodded in response and turned back to continue with the horses.

"Is it true that Bernice has been murdered?" Leone Pickup asked as the three men left the barn and crossed the farmyard heading to the house.

"Yes," Ira replied. "And her husband Harry has been done in, too. You'll see that soon enough, I'm sorry to say."

Pickup stopped the other two men just as they reached the door to the mudroom at the rear of the house. "How many people entered the house before now, Ira?"

"No one, Leone, besides me and my hired hand, William. The only other person who knows about this is Ruell Wheeler. I used his phone to place the call to your place, which is when I spoke with your wife."

"Did you or William touch anything at all, Ira? I need to know before I begin my investigation," said Pickup.

"William didn't touch one thing, and all I did was to place my hand on Harry's arm to make sure he was dead. That's it. I swear!" cried Ira.

"Now, now, calm down, man," said Pickup. "I ask only to

find out if the crime scene is intact. That's all. You're not in trouble here, Ira. Now, come on, let's go in. Since you know where you're going, you lead the way."

The trio of men entered the mudroom and then the kitchen in single file. As soon as they entered the kitchen, Deputy Sheriff Pickup and Lieutenant George reached into the inner breast pockets of their tan trench coats for pads and pencils. They scribbled furiously as they noted every detail in a visual sweep of the room.

"What's with this straw suitcase over here by the door?" Deputy Sheriff Pickup asked without directing the question at anyone in particular.

"Sure beats me!" Ira said. "I hadn't noticed it before."

Pickup noted the presence of the suitcase along with the table setting, the pots and their contents on the cook stove. He motioned to Ira to lead on and followed him through the swinging door that led to the dining room. Again the two men stopped and made notes. They both stopped writing as soon as they made out Harry's body at the foot of the stairs. They approached the body and began to write furiously again. They repeated this scene in each of the bedrooms upstairs and then made their way back down.

"Where's Bernice?" asked Pickup.

"Down in the cellar," Ira replied. "Let's go this way. It's a little quicker."

Ira led the two men over to the cellar door located near the buttery and then down the cellar stairs. When they got to where Bernice's body lay, Leone Pickup let out a short gasp and turned away at the sight. He squeezed his eyes shut, as if that would help erase the gruesome scene in front of him.

Lieutenant George placed his hand on the Deputy Sheriff's shoulder, "Are you going to be okay, Leone? Is this your first homicide investigation?"

Leone Pickup opened his eyes, turned his head to look at the Lieutenant and said in a quivering voice, "No, that's not it at all. Bernice was a close friend and a colleague of mine at the courthouse. We worked together for quite some time before she retired last December. I assumed she, too, had been shot. I wasn't prepared for this. Give me a second, would you?"

"Try and pretend you don't know her, Leone. Trust me, it'll help. I know from personal experience," advised Lieutenant George.

"Let's get back to investigating this woman's murder, eh?" Pickup said after letting out a long and sorrowful sigh.

As Pickup questioned Ira, he learned that a hired man had been living with the Farnsworths. Ira could not remember the man's name. He said he rarely spoke to the man when he saw him, and that Farnsworth always did the talking when the two men came around to his farm. When Pickup was satisfied that he would get no more information from Ira, he allowed Ira to return to the barn.

The two investigators slowly and methodically combed the length and breadth of the cellar, recording everything that could possibly be of importance to the case. Just as they were both finishing up their notes, they heard a familiar voice coming from upstairs.

"Pickup!" shouted the man, "Pickup! Where are you, man?"

"Down here in the cellar, Colonel!" Pickup shouted back at the disembodied voice from above.

A. Edward Krieger, the forty-one-year-old Cattaraugus County District Attorney, appeared at the entrance to the cellar and stood with his hands on his hips. Krieger had been commissioned as a colonel during World War I and he carried that title over into his civilian life after his discharge. Along with the title came an overbearing mantle of authority.

He and Judge Orla Black had amassed an impressive

conviction record together during their tenure in the county courthouse. The local lawbreakers called Orla "Old Hard Ass," and eventually nicknamed The Colonel "Old Hard Ass's Mouthpiece." Secretly, Orla Black and The Colonel both loved those nicknames as much as they despised the character of the men and women who were paraded daily through their courtroom. Many times, before the courtroom filled for the morning docket, one of them would tease the other and ask sarcastically, 'You ready for those big bad criminals, Old Hard Ass?' The usual reply was, 'bring on those no-gooders and you'll see how ready I am!' which elicited peals of laughter from them both as they sat in Orla's chambers drinking the coffee served to them by Bernice Kenyon.

Such lightheartedness was the exception for Colonel Krieger, who won cases due to his seriousness and dedication to detail coupled with his conception that he was a rare, sane voice standing out in a sea of insanity. He saw himself as a champion for the common people and as their advocate. In his quest to achieve the acme of those ideals, he was dogged in his pursuit of them. He pounded relentlessly at investigators, witnesses and criminals alike until he was satisfied that he had exposed the raw truth in the cases entrusted to him. He put in more time on case preparation than any other DA in upstate New York. No case was unimportant. Victim and criminal alike received justice if Colonel Krieger had his way. And he usually got his way. As a result, his persona grew in proportion to his success until he became larger than life. And so, it was inevitable that he would immediately grasp the reins in the Farnsworth homicide investigation and that he would not release them until the job was done to his satisfaction.

"Don't bother to go home tonight before leaving your full report on my desk, Deputy Pickup," The Colonel barked. "You'll fill me in on everything you know. Don't leave out one single detail, Deputy. Not one, for that one detail may be the clue that breaks this case wide open. Is this where Bernice's body lies?"

"Yes, Colonel, it is. If you could come down, sir, you'll find that it is just beyond Lieutenant George and me. I'm warning you, sir, that it is quite a gruesome sight," said Pickup.

The Colonel walked briskly around the Deputy Sheriff and Lieutenant George, and stopped when he reached Bernice's body. He knelt down on one knee, his expensive suit pants touching the dirt floor, staring intently at Bernice's body, absorbing every detail. When he was satisfied with his inspection, The Colonel spoke softly to her as if she were still alive.

"Don't you worry, Bernice," he said in a near whisper. "We'll catch whoever did this to you and your husband and I promise you I will bring them to justice. You have my word."

The Colonel went immediately into battle mode. He began barking orders at Leone Pickup and then went back upstairs to get the County Coroner, George A. Middleton. Pickup joined The Colonel upstairs and discovered that the coroner had brought deputies McDonald, Nix and Arrowsmith along with him. They were stationed around the perimeter of the house to keep others from entering the crime scene. Also present was The Colonel's Special Investigator, Elmer W. Miller, former Cattaraugus County Sheriff. Miller had already begun to process evidence. The last investigator to arrive was fingerprint expert, Elmer Lee, on loan to The Colonel from the Jamestown Police Department.

A few minutes later, they heard another vehicle drive up to the house. Two gentlemen stepped out of a car and began to remove camera equipment from the back seat. Clearly they were there to photograph the crime scene.

The Colonel went out the front door and shouted to them, "Mr. Nodler, I presume?"

"Yes, sir. Are you Colonel Krieger?" Sylvester Nodler shouted back.

"Yes! Yes! It was I who called you, sir!" The Colonel said impatiently. "Now please, be quick about setting up your equipment. As you can plainly see we are losing the light of day. We need you in the cellar immediately. Who is that with you?"

"This is Walter Wilhelm from Randolph, Colonel," Sylvester said as he put a hand on Walter's shoulder. "I called ahead for him to meet me on the highway at Price's Corners Road. I thought we might be able to get the crime scene photos before the light fails if there were two of us on the job. Walter has worked with me many times, sir. I can vouch for his qualifications as a proficient photographer."

"Very well, man," retorted The Colonel. "But, I want you in the basement and Wilhelm can take the photographs in the living room. I will personally select the angles and distances for the photos myself, understood?"

"Absolutely, sir," Sylvester affirmed. "Just give us a few minutes and we'll get set up."

The Colonel accompanied Sylvester down to the cellar after providing instructions to Walter for the photos of Harry's body. Satisfied that the task of photographing the crime scene in the basement was well in hand, The Colonel went back upstairs and debriefed Leone Pickup. When that was done, he sent Pickup out to perform the field investigation.

"Hit all the houses in the area and get statements from the occupants," ordered The Colonel. "Find someone who knows the name of the Farnsworth's hired hand and determine when he was seen last. I want a name today, Leone. Now go out and get it for me!"

Pickup found Lieutenant George and borrowed the key to his car. He walked out the Farnsworth's front door and headed for the dirt road, but he heard a faint voice call out his name. Glancing over his shoulder, Pickup saw Ira Bennett waving to him from the barn door. He walked through the deep snow to where Ira stood.

"Lindsay is his name," Ira said to Leone Pickup. "The Farnsworth's hired hand was named Alfred Lindsay. Most people called him Fred or Freddy. Hope that helps. Can't say that we remember anything else about him, as William and I barely spoke to the man."

Pickup thanked Ira and ran back across the farmyard to the house and informed The Colonel and Lieutenant George that they had a name for the missing man. It was decided that the lieutenant would drive Leone Pickup back to Little Valley so Pickup could get his vehicle. Lieutenant George would head out for the State Trooper's Post in Friendship, and issue a General Alarm for one Alfred Lindsay, also known as Fred Lindsay, AKA Freddy Lindsay, as soon as possible.

Deputy Sheriff Pickup and Lieutenant George decided it would be prudent to wait until the lieutenant arrived at the Friendship Post rather than placing the General Alarm by phone. Pickup was counting on getting as many interviews as possible before the lieutenant reached the State Trooper Post. The Friendship Post was about ten miles beyond the town of Cuba, near Highway 17. They estimated the Lieutenant would arrive there around 7:15 that evening, which gave Pickup a good two hours to gather information before the Alarm went out.

But first, Pickup, who was not one to shirk responsibility, did the last thing in the world he wanted to do. He took a deep breath, looked up a phone number in a Salamanca telephone book and placed a call.

The phone rang three times before a man answered. "Hello! Blessing Photography Studio. Lynn Blessing speaking."

"Hello, Lynn. It's Leone Pickup. Are you with a customer right now?"

"No, I'm free, Leone. What can I do for you today? Someone needs a photo taken, I hope?"

"No, Lynn, nothing like that. I'm afraid that I have some bad news. Are you sitting down, Lynn?"

"Why, yes, as a matter of fact I am sitting down. What's this all about, Leone? Has someone been hurt?"

"Worse than that. Much worse, I'm afraid. There is no good way to deliver this kind of news, so I am just going to give it to you as it is, Lynn. I just got back from Bernice's farm in Coldspring and I am sorry to inform you that she has been murdered."

There was complete silence at the other end of the phone and a long moment passed before Lynn responded. "Murdered? Murdered, you said? I knew that Farnsworth man was up to no good when he married her! We begged her not to do it, but you know Bernice! She had her mind made up and that was it. Have you got him in custody?"

"No, no! You misunderstand, Lynn. Harry Farnsworth has been murdered, also. It looks like the hired hand might have done it. He's missing and we're looking for information about him before we put out an alarm. All we've got right now is his name. Is his name Alfred Lindsay?"

"Give me a second would you, please. My head is literally swimming with the news. Oh, my God! Bernice... murdered! Oh, my God! How will I break the news to Edith? It will devastate her. You know how close those two are, or... were?"

"Yes, I do. Bernice and I spent a lot of time together when she worked at the courthouse. We got to know each other very well over the years. May I please extend my condolences to your family, Lynn? I am very sorry for the loss of your sister-in-law."

"Thank you, Leone. Thank you very much. I will do that."

"Very good, Lynn. I hate to press you, but time is of the essence. We need to get as much information on Alfred Lindsey as we can in the next couple of hours in order to catch him. I need a description of him. What can you tell me?"

"Well, let me think. Bernice called him Freddy when she

spoke of him, but I don't know that she ever mentioned his last name. I would say he is a young man. I figure maybe twenty-two or twenty-three years old, brown stick-straight hair, usually wore a knit cap and talked with a New England accent. Does that help?"

"Yes, absolutely it does. How would you describe his build—his height and his weight?"

"I'm not a very good judge of that, but here goes. I would say that he was of a muscular build, very lean, maybe five-foot-six or seven in height, and about 140 to 150 pounds in weight. But I am only guessing."

"That's fine, Lynn. It matches the description I got from Ira Bennett and his hired hand pretty closely. Thanks, Lynn. You've been a big help."

"You're welcome. I'm glad the call came from you. Bernice spoke well of you and often. Can I ask one thing?" Lynn said.

"Certainly, you may. What is it?"

"Did she suffer? I mean, did Bernice suffer before she died. Edith will want to know."

"No, she didn't suffer, Lynn. The coroner said she did not suffer at all. She never knew what hit her."

"And one more thing you haven't mentioned, Leone, how was she murdered?"

Leone Pickup grimaced and mentally cursed his luck for not getting off the phone sooner. He took in a deep breath and exhaled before he replied. "She was killed with an axe. Her murderer almost cut her head off, Lynn. It was the most horrific thing I ever laid eyes on. Please don't let Edith view the body. It will haunt her for the rest of her life. I know it will haunt me for a long, long time."

Pickup could hear Lynn sobbing into the phone. He waited until the sobbing subsided. "Again, Lynn, I am very sorry for your loss. You will need to contact the coroner's office on Monday in order to release her body. Her autopsy should have been completed by then. I am on my way back to Coldspring now. We think the murderer stole Bernice's Coupe. I'll keep you posted on our progress. Goodbye, Lynn."

"Yes, goodbye, Leone. And thank you again. I know this call must have been a most difficult task for you."

Leone Pickup hung up the phone and wished that Sheriff Carlson had not left him in charge when he'd been called away to Olean earlier that morning to testify at a hearing. Pickup's excitement at having been given a chance to show that he could be an effective leader had vanished at the Farnsworth's farm earlier in the afternoon.

But without wasting a moment, Pickup left the Sheriff's Office, got into his car and headed back to Coldspring. His first stop was at Nora Moynihan's home where she provided details concerning Freddy's movements up to the evening of Monday, March 4. She also described the unusual tattoos Freddy had on his hands. Pickup's other interviews yielded scant information and nothing of Freddy's movements after Monday evening.

Deputy Sheriff Pickup returned to the Sheriff's Office at seven o'clock that evening. The Colonel, his Special Investigator, the coroner, Sheriff Lester Carlson, and the extra deputies had returned with the bodies of Harry and Bernice a half an hour earlier.

Colonel Krieger was disappointed to find that Pickup's interviews had yielded so few facts about the man. The Colonel contributed the make, model, and license number of Bernice's car, information which had been obtained from the Department of Motor Vehicles in Little Valley. Pickup wrote up the report for the General Alarm and then called Lieutenant George in Friendship and dictated the information. Lieutenant George immediately typed the information and handed it to State Trooper Mousseau, who transmitted it statewide. The General Alarm read:

```
72 file 12   SP   Friendship   Mar 8-35
To     GA     Code Signal 33
     Wanted for double murder: Alfred
Lindsay, 23-5-7-150, dark brown or black
hair, dark eyes, tattoo marks on back of
left hand, tattoo marks on back of each
finger of left hand between second and
third joints, French Canadian, talks with a
New England accent. Wearing dark trousers,
laced knee-hi boots, red top woolen
stockings, black tam with tassel. Murders
occurred at Coldspring, Cattaraugus County,
NY, in the AM of March 6-35.
     This subject has been thought to have
stolen the Victim's car, a 1930 Chevrolet
Sport Coupe, color green, wire wheels,
License No. 3H-71-13 NY, Motor No. 1809585,
Serial number 12AD47873 and may be headed
for his home in State of Vermont. Arrest,
hold and notify.
     Auth. Dep. Shrf., Leone Pickup, Catt
Co, NY Mousseau       7*35 PM
```

As soon as the General Alarm was sent, hundreds of law-enforcement dispatchers broadcast it to every patrol car equipped with a two-way radio in New York State and beyond. The seven-state manhunt for Freddy Lindsay had begun.

CHAPTER THREE

LYNN BLESSING PLACED THE PHONE RECEIVER DOWN GENTLY onto its cradle. He cupped his face in his hands and rested his elbows on his desk. He sat that way for a few minutes, then stood and looked around. Everything in the back room of his photography studio seemed surreal. He felt detached from his surroundings. With a few slow and deliberate steps he reached the door that led into the studio. He stopped at the doorframe and leaned against it, staring at the backwards words on his large front window. Large, gilt letters spelled out the name of his business. He was barely aware of the late afternoon bustle beyond the window as the citizens of Salamanca rushed about their everyday business. He swooned, brought his hand to his forehead and noticed a loud buzzing noise inside his head. The news he had just received from Leone Pickup was sending him into mild shock. He heard Leone's voice repeat the same phrase over and over. 'She has been murdered. Bernice has been murdered.'

The old photographer moved like an automaton as he crossed the studio floor to remove his coat from the peg of the coat rack. Unconscious of what he was doing, he slipped his arms into the coat sleeves and turned up his collar. He opened the shop door, walked out, and closed it behind him, forgetting to lock it.

Lynn Blessing walked up Main to River Street and turned right. Slowly his vertigo subsided and his senses returned by the time he reached the home he shared with Edith, his wife. He stopped at the gate to the front yard, placed his right hand on the latch and stared up at the house. For the first time in his life he did not want to walk to the front door and enter. He did not want to be the bearer of the news of Bernice's death. He abhorred unpleasantness of any sort. He felt resentment for Bernice, but resigned himself to what he must do. He would need to be both the destroyer and the restorer of Edith's broken heart.

As he continued to stand at the gate he realized the mantle of power in the Blessing-Kenyon family had changed. Bernice had been the family's matriarch. With Bernice's death, power would now be foisted upon him and the thought increased his feeling of resentment. Power and responsibility were the last things Lynn wanted.

Finally, Lynn walked up to the front door and entered his home. Edith greeted him from the parlor and began to chatter about dinner and her day. Lynn raised his hand, signaling that she should stop talking.

"Why, Lynn Blessing!" Edith said, "how absolutely rude of you to cut me off in that manner!"

Lynn leaned over and gave Edith a small kiss on the lips and said, "Edith, darling, please sit down. I have some very bad news that I regret having to deliver to you."

"Oh, dear!" Edith exclaimed. "We're financially destitute, aren't we? I have secretly worried about it for months. Whatever shall we do? Wherever shall we go?"

"No, my dear," Lynn said reassuringly. "It's nothing like that. I find myself without the words to say this well. I suppose that is because there is no good way to say this. Edith, I am truly sorry to tell you that your sister Bernice has been murdered along with her husband, Harold, on their farm."

Edith's eyes widened and her mouth fell open. At first, the news did not register. It took a few moments for the real portent of what Lynn said to sink in. Edith stood, stumbled over to Lynn and threw herself into his arms as she burst into tears.

Lynn held her tightly and rubbed her back, letting her cry. When her sobs subsided, he guided her back to her overstuffed parlor chair and helped her sit down.

"Did she suffer? Who is responsible?" Edith asked.

"Leone Pickup called me at the studio and he said she never knew what hit her. And the absolute worst part of it, my dear, is that she was killed with an axe. More than that, I do not know. Leone told me only about the axe and that they believe the hired hand, Freddy, is the one who murdered them both. Apparently, he has stolen Bernice's car but no one knows where he's gone. Leone said he was heading out looking for witnesses and information about Freddy and that he was going to put out a General Alarm."

"Bernice's marriage to an ex-convict was a bad idea," Edith said between sobs. "I begged her to give that man, Harry, some money and send him on his way! If only Bernice had listened! If only she'd listened to me! And now, she's gone. Gone! I can't believe it. I can't believe she's dead!"

Edith broke down again and Lynn did his best to console her. He suggested that she go upstairs and lie down. Edith agreed and walked to the stairway that led to the upper floor of their house. But she turned suddenly and said, "What about Olive and Bobby? Shouldn't we let them know what happened to their aunt?"

"Yes, of course. I'll tell them as soon as they get home. But I think I should take it easy on Bobby."

Edith solemnly agreed and climbed the stairs, forgetting about the dinner warming in the oven. Lynn remained in the parlor and waited for his children to return home. Olive was twenty-two; Bobby, their son, was eleven. When they arrived, Lynn sat them down and told them Bernice had been murdered. Olive sat quietly, obviously shocked. Bobby didn't know what to do, so first he looked at the floor, then asked to be excused. Lynn provided a few more details for Olive, but she too went up to her room, leaving Lynn alone in the parlor. He sighed, and then stood to perform the last task of reluctant informer.

Lynn called for a cab to pick him up and take him to Morna

and Dora Kenyon's house located on Broad Street in Salamanca. Lynn spoke of Bernice's death and Morna and Dora were understandably staggered by the news. Lynn stayed long enough to make sure the sisters would be all right, then left for home again.

After Lynn's departure, the news of Bernice's death cast a pall over Morna and Dora's home. Bernice had been an integral part of their lives. Morna and Dora, Bernice's two maiden sisters, had been living vicariously through Bernice as she rose in social status in Cattaraugus County. They had basked in her glory as it overflowed onto them. Now that was she gone, they realized their social status and financial support were gone as well. Fear and grief settled quickly in the home that Bernice had so generously bought for them. For the first time in their lives, they had no one to take care of them. They knew that Edith and Lynn could not take over where Bernice had left off. The two sisters huddled together for support on their divan until it was time for bed. Sleep did not come for either of them that night.

Hundreds of miles away, Freddy Lindsay walked up to his sister's house in New Rochelle. It had taken most of the day for him to hitchhike a mere twenty-five miles. The trip was punctuated with a few rides and several long, monotonous walks. He retold himself a story he conjured up during the walks and rang the doorbell of 9 Sixth Street, Helen and Michael Short's house. After a long pause, he saw the light come on in the living room window. Then Freddy was startled when the porch light flicked on. The door opened halfway. Helen stood in front of him.

"Freddy!" she exclaimed. "My gosh, you look terrible. What are you doing in New Rochelle? I thought you were working at that farm upstate."

"I quit workin' for them a few days ago. They couldn't pay me for last month's work so I up and left. I've been hitchhiking for days," he lied. "Can I come in?"

"Yes, of course you can!" Helen said as she swung the door open further so that he could enter.

"Where's Michael?" Freddy asked as he scanned the living room.

"He's pulling a second shift at the shop tonight. They're shorthanded at work. The flu has kept half of their work force at home in bed. Michael won't be home for another hour and a half. Good Lord, Freddy! When was the last time you bathed? Let's get you into a bathtub and we'll catch up when I can stand having you in the same room with me!"

The bath proved cathartic for Freddy. His troubles and the terrible deed he had done were temporarily tucked away into a remote corner of his brain. He basked in the love that flowed unconditionally from his sister. Helen fussed and clucked over him like a mother hen. When he stepped from the tub, she had a complete change of clothes laid out for him. Although Michael was a little larger in build than Freddy was, Michael's clothes fit him pretty well. Freddy slicked his wet hair back with a comb he found in a drawer and headed for the kitchen.

"Ah, now that's more like it!" Helen said when Freddy entered the room. "I'll bet you haven't eaten for a while either, have you, Freddy? Are you out of money?"

"No, I've got plenty to last me a while," he lied again.

"So, what's your plan now?" Helen probed, "I hope you're not planning on staying here with us, Freddy. I don't think I could stand the friction between you and Michael under the same roof again."

"No, I've got something brewing down in Florida. I met a guy when I was hitchhiking down here and he wants me to help him drive his car to Florida. I figure I can catch a job after I get there. And I think a change of scenery might do me good."

"That's good news, Freddy. Now, don't get me wrong! It's not that I don't want you here, you know. It's just that I have to be loyal to my husband. And it's not that I don't love you, either. But, he is my husband and if I have to choose between you two, it's gotta be him. I hope you understand that. You do, don't you?"

A smile spread across Freddy's face. "Sure, I understand, Helen. He's your husband and he's gotta be number one. You got a good guy for a husband, you know. Don't you think for a minute that I don't appreciate that he has taken in our little sister, Mary, and raised her like she was his own. By the way, where is Mary? I thought that she would be down here giving me the third degree already."

"She's in bed. I think it would be better if you see her in the morning. She won't sleep a wink once she knows her favorite brother is here!"

Helen and Freddy chatted until they were interrupted by Michael Short's arrival. Michael walked into the living room carrying his lunch pail. He looked tired and grumpy. He stiffened visibly when he saw Freddy in the kitchen. But before he could say a word, Helen informed him that Freddy was there for the night only and would be leaving for Florida the next day. Michael looked relieved and his body posture relaxed. He was embarrassed to have Freddy in his home. He often wondered what his family and friends would say if they knew that his wife's brother was an ex-convict. That was the wedge that divided the two men. And it could never be removed.

The trio ate a very late supper together and retired for the night. Freddy laid down on the couch in the living room and slept soundly for the first time in days. However, it proved to be a brief respite from the fear and worry that had kept him sleepless. Nagging emotions woke with him on Saturday morning, March 9. His thoughts brought back the nervous tension. He needed to move on.

Helen and Michael rose early to get Michael ready for another double shift at the shop. Freddy stayed in the living room, waiting for Michael to leave. Freddy said goodbye as Michael walked through the living room on his way out. But Michael barely acknowledged Freddy as he kissed Helen and left.

Freddy got up and went upstairs to wake his thirteen-year-old sister, Mary. She screeched with delight when she recognized Freddy. The three siblings spent the rest of the day laughing and talking. They reminisced about old friends, old neighborhoods and the good times associated with them. The time flew by and before they knew it they were startled by the slap of the evening newspaper as it hit the front porch.

"Can you believe it?" Helen exclaimed. "It's six o'clock already! Let's have sandwiches for supper and call it good, shall we? By the way, what time are you planning to leave, Freddy?"

"Well. I need to be back in the city tonight so I guess anytime soon would work. How about packing that sandwich? I can take it with me and eat it later."

Mary pleaded with Freddy to stay a while longer, but he declined. It tugged at his heart when he lied about coming back to see her soon. As with Madeline, he knew this was the last time he would see his little sister, and that realization sat like lead in the pit of his stomach.

The day was transitioning towards darkness as Freddy left Helen's house. He turned and waved goodbye to them when he reached the sidewalk. As he began to walk down Sixth Street he noticed a dark sedan pull down the street and park directly across the street from him. The two male occupants in the car stared intently at him as he walked by. Freddy threw a thin smile their way and continued at a steady pace down the street. When he got to the corner of Union and Sixth Streets he encountered another dark sedan with two male occupants. They, too, stared him down as he passed their vehicle. And again he appeared as if they were of no consequence to him even though he was about to crawl out of his skin with fear.

Continuing up Sixth Street, Freddy came to Washington Street and stuck his thumb out. Within a few minutes he secured a ride and was on his way back to New York City. Unknown to him, he had just walked through a dragnet that the New Rochelle Police Department had laid out for him.

Unmarked police cars were waiting on Union Street, Seventh, Sixth, and Fifth streets. They had received a wire from Lieutenant George detailing the addresses of persons Freddy had corresponded with when he was incarcerated at Sing Sing. Helen's New Rochelle address was on that list. Possessing no photo of Freddy, the police were relying on finding Bernice's Sport Coupe as an indication of his presence on Sixth Street. They were not looking for a man traveling by foot.

When New Rochelle Police Department Detective Vincent Lewis knocked on Helen's front door he received no answer. As he peered through the living room window he could see Helen sitting in the living room. She was staring at the evening paper that lay on the coffee table in front of her. One hand covered her mouth.

Helen had the paper open to page 32. She was reading an article that said:

```
Farmhand Is Sought In Killing Of Couple
Was Prison Friend of Man Slain in
Cattaraugus Hills,
Who Had Discharged Him
Randolph, N. Y., March 9, 1935 (AP)—
Albert J. Lindsay, prison pal of one Harold
Farnsworth, who was slain with his wife on
their farm near here, was sought after word
was broadcasted that he was wanted for
questioning in the crime.
```

When Detective Lewis knocked on the door again, Helen rose and crossed the room to answer it. When she saw the detective's badge she asked him to come in and motioned towards a chair in the living room. The detective sat down opposite her.

"You just missed him, detective," Helen interrupted matter-of-factly. "He left about five minutes ago. I'm surprised you didn't see him on your way down Sixth Street. Can we start off with getting his name right, please? His name is not Albert. It's Alfred. My brother's name is Alfred Joseph Lindsay."

CHAPTER FOUR

COMMUNICATIONS BETWEEN THE FRIENDSHIP STATE TROOPER Post and the New Rochelle Police Department flew back and forth at a furious pace until it was determined that Freddy had vanished after strolling through a well laid out dragnet. Armed with fresh information culled from Helen, Freddy's sister, the focus of the manhunt shifted to New York City. They may as well have been searching for a needle in a proverbial haystack. They were searching for one man walking around an area of three hundred and five square miles, populated by almost seven million people.

On Saturday, March 9, 1935, Sheriff Carlson, Colonel Krieger, Deputy Sheriff Leone Pickup, and State Trooper Lieutenant George met at 7:15 p.m. at the Sheriff's Office. They listened attentively as Lieutenant George reported on the near miss in New Rochelle. A secretary took notes. The consensus was that there was little they could do except wait for Lindsay to surface somewhere between New York City and the State of Florida. Each man left the brief meeting determined to do everything and anything to bring about the capture of Freddy Lindsay.

Lynn Blessing, in the meantime, called Judge Orla Black at his home in Salamanca. Orla had been his family's attorney for more years than either could remember. He waited patiently, counting the number of rings. Orla answered at ring number five.

"Hello," Orla said.

"Hello, Orla. This is Lynn Blessing. I hope you will forgive me for calling so late, but this matter is urgent."

"Yes, I know," Orla said. "I should have called you, Lynn, but to be honest I didn't know what to say. You know that I am absolutely shocked and enormously saddened at what happened to Bernice. I still can't believe it."

"Thank you, Orla. I was wondering if you would have the time to help me secure the release of Bernice's body from the coroner's office tonight or tomorrow morning. I have no experience in these kinds of matters. Also, I think that it would be in order to begin settling Bernice's estate now, rather than later, don't you agree?"

"On the matter of the coroner, say no more. I will handle everything this evening by phone. In the matter of Bernice's estate, we will have to clear up one important fact before we can file in the Surrogate Court. Who died first, Lynn? Was it Bernice or Harold Farnsworth? That has to be determined before anything else."

"I don't believe we know who died first, Orla. What difference does that make?"

"Oh, it makes plenty of difference! That fact alone will determine whose family is entitled to the estate. For example, if Bernice died first, then Harry is heir to her part of their estate. When Harry is murdered it puts his family in line to inherit the entire estate. Or it could be vice versa."

"Oh, bother! Already this is becoming a problem, Orla. Between you and me, I really resent having to be the one to settle Bernice's affairs. I feel that Bernice brought this on herself by marrying a felon. She married a common felon, Orla! What kind of sane person does that, I ask you!"

"Lynn, you need to put this in perspective. Bernice was a woman who had to live her life her way, that's all."

"Well, that's fine for Bernice, but what about me? She got to live her life as she saw fit, and now she's left the pieces for me to pick up!"

"Lynn, you're upset now and your resentment is quite understandable. However, as your attorney, I need to deal with the unemotional aspects of the legal problems we now find at hand. Let's try to deal with this on that level, shall we?"

"Yes, yes. You won't hear another word from me on the subject. I guess I just needed to get it off my chest. What do I need to do to proceed?"

"Let me handle this from now on, Lynn. I'll contact The Colonel this evening and we'll discuss the results of his investigation. Do you have any contact information for Farnsworth's family?"

"No, at least not that I know of right now. That reminds me of something. I will also need to know when I can gain entry to the house to start cataloging the contents for auction. Also, I know they owed money on the farm and that's due and payable upon their death, isn't it?"

"Yes, that's correct for sure. It's a common clause found in almost all mortgage agreements and land contracts. I'll address the entry issue with The Colonel and let you know when he and the sheriff will grant you permission to enter the house. Perhaps you can find some contact information for Farnsworth's family among his personal effects when you go there. One more thing, what funeral home do want Bernice released to and do you want to have Harry transferred with her as well?"

"Oh, my! I hadn't even thought much about Harry's body. Hopefully, their estate will be able to bear the brunt of the cost for his burial as well as Bernice's. If it's allowed, have him transported with her. After all, they were husband and wife and I suppose that's the decent thing to do. Send them over to Myers and Myers Funeral Home in Randolph. I have made arrangements with them."

"Very good, Lynn. I will get back to you with my progress tomorrow morning. Please pass on my deepest regrets to Edith for me. Goodbye, Lynn."

"Yes. Goodbye, Orla."

Orla Black went back to finish a late supper with his wife, and Lynn Blessing returned to the state of mourning that enveloped his house.

Meanwhile, Freddy Lindsay was walking away from the El train in New York City. He had arrived back in the city at one o'clock Sunday morning and headed directly for the nearest El station. As he had done several days prior, he rode the train, back and forth, for hours. Hunger was the only thing that drove him out of the cocoon-like protection the train provided.

On one of his forays in search of food, Freddy entered a small restaurant and sat down at the counter. He placed his order for coffee and a doughnut with a waitress who never even glanced up to look at him. Freddy looked around the near-empty restaurant for a newspaper and spotted a half-folded front section on the counter near the cash register. He went over and picked it up. When he returned to his stool, he skimmed the front page and sipped at his coffee.

One article screamed the news about striking elevator operators and building service workers in the Bronx who went berserk and destroyed the lobbies of several commercial buildings. Freddy ignored the article and searched the rest of the section page by page. Then he saw it. Inside the back page was the story about the murders of Bernice and Harold Farnsworth. He gulped down his coffee, grabbed the doughnut, and fumbled for change. He threw down an amount close to what he figured he owed and ran out of the restaurant with the newspaper in hand.

Freddy felt naked. He avoided making eye contact with passers-by. He looked down at his hands and was horrified when he realized he was a marked man. He passed a men's haberdashery and entered, purchasing the least expensive pair of gloves he could find.

Panicked, Freddy headed again for the anonymity of the El. He read the newspaper article over and over until he knew its contents by heart. He stayed on the train until late in the evening. Tired of sitting, Freddy decided it was time to rent a room for the evening. He entered a flophouse on Manhattan Avenue that sported a sign in the window touting fifty-cent rooms.

Freddy registered under his favorite alias, Arthur Flynn. After paying for the room, he walked up the stairs to the second floor. He slipped the key into the lock and then stood there, motionless, unable to enter. He had visions of policemen bursting through the hotel room door with pistols blazing. He jerked the key out of the lock and headed back down the stairs to ground level. The bored and uninterested hotel clerk did not notice him as he walked out through the lobby door.

Abandoning any thought of occupying the room he had rented, Freddy took to the streets and wandered the city without direction. He tossed the room key into a trashcan. When his feet began to ache, he headed for the subway instead of the elevated train. He had begun to recognize some of the passengers on the El, and that made him believe they surely recognized him, too. To avoid those familiar faces, Freddy made his way to the fresh anonymity of a subway line.

When he reached the subway platform and a train arrived, he boarded the last car and sat down. His stomach growled for nourishment and it forced him out of his seat in search of discarded food. He walked though each subway car and was rewarded with a small bit of a candy bar in a wrinkled wrapper under a seat. He consumed the candy and returned to spend the rest of the night in the back car.

Sleep came to Freddy in the same manner it had on the El train. That is, it came in fits and spurts. His paranoia had increased tenfold after the discovery of the newspaper article in the *Times,* so whenever his head nodded with sleep, he would jerk himself awake and scan the passengers in the subway car. He was on a constant lookout for the police. After a few hours of this futile battle, his body succumbed to its need for rest and he fell into a deep sleep.

Sweating as if the subway car were on fire, Freddy awoke in a panic early on Monday morning, March 11. He had been dreaming that the police caught up with him and were dragging him towards a paddy wagon parked at a distance. As he dreamed, his arms and legs thrashed about, enacting his attempt to escape from their grip. Fortunately, he was alone in the subway car when he awoke. Shaken by the vivid dream, Freddy paced through the nearly deserted cars several times. His panicked brain was locked with fear and it rendered him inept. As in the days previous, Freddy could not come up with a plan for escape. And, to make matters worse, he was almost out of money.

Hunger once again drove Freddy out onto the street around ten o'clock in the morning. He searched trashcans in back alleys but he could not bring himself to eat any of the foul smelling food he found in them. He wandered the streets of Manhattan, hoping a solution would land in his lap. Finally, around noon, he gave into his hunger pangs and entered Rector's Restaurant on Seventh Avenue and Forty-Fourth Street. He ordered a sandwich and a glass of beer with the last of the money he had lifted from Bernice's purse on March 5.

Freddy tried to eat his sandwich with his gloves on, but that proved a difficult task and he didn't want to make a spectacle of himself. Without realizing it, he drew the attention of two men in dark suits sitting one table away from him. As soon as Freddy removed his gloves to eat his sandwich, one of the men whispered into the ear of his companion and both sets of eyes fixed themselves on Freddy, who ate his sandwich unaware he was being intently watched.

Freddy wolfed down his sandwich and then lingered over the glass of beer in order to occupy the table for a little while longer. When he drained his glass of the last drop he stood up, left his money on the table, and made for the front door of the restaurant. Detectives John Notheis and Walter Clancy of the West Thirtieth Street Police Station got up from their table, signaled to the waiter to be quiet, flashed their badges, and left without paying for their meals. They followed Freddy at a safe distance for a few blocks to see if he would join up with anyone. Seeing that he was walking without purpose, the detectives overtook him and each clamped onto one of his arms. Freddy's heart dropped into his stomach. He turned beet red and tried to squirm out of their grip.

"Hey!" shouted Freddy, "Let me go! What's going on here?"

"I'll tell you what's going on here, Bob Lindsay! You're under arrest for bank robbery! Now come along peacefully, will ya?"

Now that he was in the hands of the police his mind instinctively began to work like a fine-tuned clock. He surmised that these policemen thought they were arresting his brother, Henry Robert Lindsay. Unknown to Freddy, Bob had recently robbed a theater box office on Broadway with his gang of thieves and had gotten cleanly away with ten thousand dollars in cash. Neither Freddy nor his family had seen or heard from Bob in over five years.

Freddy threw a Hail Mary pass and prayed it would work as he said, "No! You guys have the wrong person! My name is Arthur Flynn. I never heard of a Bob Lindsay, I swear it!"

"Nah," growled Detective Notheis. "I'm not buyin' that! I recognized you back there in the restaurant, all right. I've got a good memory for faces I see on wanted posters. And I vaguely remembered something about those tattoos of yours, too. You're going down to the station for questioning, buddy."

Notheis slammed Freddy's chest against the wall of a brick building and held him there while his partner, Walter Clancy, put the handcuffs on Freddy's wrists. They hailed a taxi and took Freddy to the West Sixty-Eighth Street police station. There they immediately placed him in an interrogation room but made him wait alone for forty-five long minutes to soften him up before Deputy Inspector Michael E. McDermott entered the room and began the questioning. Notheis and Clancy stood watching from the other side of a two-way mirror.

Inspector McDermott was a pro when it came to interrogation. He tried several tactics before he found that intimidation was the best method to use on Freddy. He threatened him and he bullied him. He called him a big liar and a common thief. He showed him an old picture of Bob Lindsay and insisted that it was a picture of him. He battered Freddy for thirty minutes before he finally saw some cracks appear around the seams.

"Look, here, man!" McDermott shouted as he slammed the palm of his hand down on the wooden table that separated him from Freddy, "For the last time! You are not Arthur Flynn, are you?"

Freddy, tired and sorely in need of a good night's rest, slumped forward in his chair and let out a big breath of air. McDermott waited silently for Freddy's response.

"No," Freddy said quietly, "You're right. My name is not Arthur Flynn. My name is Alfred Lindsay and I'm wanted for murder in Randolph, New York." Freddy paused, looked up at McDermott wistfully and said, "I'm glad it's over."

The revelation stunned Inspector McDermott. He sat across from Freddy for several seconds before the confession fell into place. McDermott finally recalled seeing a General Alarm the day before concerning a murder suspect at large from Randolph, New York. McDermott bolted from the room and locked the door behind him. Detectives Notheis and Clancy joined him in searching for the General Alarm paperwork. The police station buzzed as word of Freddy's capture spread.

McDermott, Notheis and Clancy went back to the interrogation room to talk with Freddy. Their prime focus now lay in obtaining a statement from him before he clammed up. They needed a statement in lieu of legal proof of his identification.

McDermott's tactics changed radically. His temperament cooled and he treated Freddy like a guest. He offered him a cigarette and a bottle of soda pop. He ordered in a sandwich and they made small talk while Freddy ate it. He talked to Freddy as if they were buddies. And, most importantly, he flattered Freddy by saying how impressed he was by Freddy's display of courage in coming clean about his real identity. He called him a "real stand-up kind of guy."

Slowly and expertly the inspector gained Freddy's trust and the three of them began to write out Freddy's statement for him. When the wording was done to Freddy's satisfaction, the confession was sent to a typist who returned it to them in the interrogation room.

Inspector McDermott handed two sheets of paper to Freddy and said, "Here's the statement we helped you to draw up today, Freddy. Now I want to advise you that you're holding a very important document in your hand. You want to be sure that what is typed in it is exactly what you want to say. If there is anything that you don't want in there or you feel is incorrect in anyway, you just let us know. We'll change it right away before we have you sign it. You understand that, Freddy?"

"Yeah, sure," Freddy replied. "I understand."

Freddy read both pages slowly and then he read them once again. Satisfied with the content of the statement, Freddy signed his full name at the bottom of both pages. It was 7:15 p.m. when he handed the pages back to Inspector McDermott.

The inspector turned to detectives Notheis and Clancy and said, "He's your prize, detectives. Book him in as on-hold for the Cattaraugus County DA."

CHAPTER FIVE

NEWS OF FREDDY'S CAPTURE TRAVELED FAST. THE TELETYPE AT the State Trooper Friendship Post chattered off the details of his arrest at 7:30 that evening. State Trooper Mousseau ripped the message off the machine and ran back to find Lieutenant George. The lieutenant called out the announcement that Alfred Joseph Lindsay had been captured. A great shout went up among the men as they clapped one another on the back. The manhunt for Bernice's murderer had been regarded as an internal matter for them. Bernice's years of service at the County Courthouse had served to elevate Bernice's status in the manhunt for Freddy. Bernice had been one of their own.

As soon as the men quieted down, Lieutenant George called Sheriff Carlson and gave him the news. Sheriff Carlson in turn called Colonel Krieger at home. They decided to travel together to New York City with Special Investigator Elmer Miller and Lieutenant George to pick up Freddy. Deputy Sheriff Leone Pickup was unavailable, as he was in North Carolina collecting an arrested fugitive for return to Cattaraugus County for prosecution.

The sheriff called Elmer Miller and Lieutenant George while The Colonel packed, kissed his wife goodbye, and drove his car to Little Valley to pick up the paper warrant for Alfred Lindsay's arrest. It had been issued on Saturday, March 10, 1935 by Rollin Pratt, Justice of the Peace for Little Valley. The Colonel knew from experience that the NYPD would not release their prisoner without the warrant.

The Colonel met his traveling companions at the parking lot across the street from the courthouse. They loaded their suitcases into the trunk of The Colonel's 1934 Cadillac four-door sedan, drove out of Little Valley and headed for Highway 17.

They reached New York City in the early morning hours of Tuesday, March 12. The Colonel brought his car to a stop at the curb of the New Yorker Hotel, located at 481 Eighth Avenue. The men piled out of the car and retrieved their suitcases from its trunk. A parking valet handed The Colonel a paper receipt and whisked his car away to a private garage.

The four men entered the hotel's palatial lobby through the main door. Elmer Miller and Lieutenant George were awestruck at the grandeur. The hotel was huge beyond belief. With twenty-five hundred rooms, it was the largest hotel in New York City. It also boasted multiple ballrooms, ten private dining salons, five world-class restaurants manned by thirty-five chefs, a forty-two seat barber shop with twenty manicurists, ninety-two telephone operators, and one hundred and fifty laundry workers who processed up to three hundred and fifty thousand pieces of laundry every day.

The Colonel went to the hotel desk and handled the acquisition of rooms. When he returned to his companions, he passed out room keys and instructed them to rendezvous in the hotel lobby again at noon, after a few hours of sleep. They rode up in the elevator and bade one another good night.

Lieutenant George let out a loud whistle when he opened the door to his room. He had never seen such opulence. He marveled at the feel of the silk sheets on the bed when he slipped between them, but felt a pang of guilt when he realized that this luxury came at Bernice's expense. As he closed his eyes, the image of Bernice's partially decapitated head loomed in his mind's eye. Sleep did not come quickly to the lieutenant for the fourth night in a row.

All four men met in the lobby at noon. The Colonel shepherded them into a private dining salon that he had reserved.

Lieutenant George took one look at the assortment of eating utensils that lay on both sides of four plates and felt most uncomfortable. "Good Lord, Colonel!" Lieutenant George exclaimed. "Is this dinner or surgery? I've never seen so many knives, forks and spoons in my life! I'm not ashamed to admit that I have no idea how to use them, or when to use them."

"Calm yourself, lieutenant," said The Colonel with a little laugh. "I'll let you know when to use them. We're in a private dining salon and no one is watching. Sit down! You'll do just fine."

Lieutenant George didn't budge. "Colonel, that's fine about the silverware, but there is something else bothering me. Isn't this finery costing the county a bit much? I'm not comfortable with spending the taxpayer's money like this."

The Colonel laughed again. "I like you, Lieutenant George, and I admire your forthrightness. However, the fact is I am paying for everything above and beyond the county per diem I was given for your expenses by the county treasurer. I am not accustomed to staying in lesser accommodations and I am not comfortable staying here while you three stay in a sub-standard hotel. So, the only solution is to have you stay here also and for me to pay the difference myself. And it is my pleasure to do so. So, again, please lieutenant, sit down and let's order our lunch. We have a lot to discuss before we get to the West Sixty-Eighth Street Police Station this afternoon."

"Thank you for your generosity, Colonel," said Lieutenant George. "I feel much more comfortable here as your guest."

The room was staffed by three waiters who attended to their every need. They took the men's lunch orders and served coffee while the men waited for their meals to arrive. The Colonel wasted no time getting down to business. As an officer, he had acquired and honed a fine set of organizational skills and he applied them to his work for the county where they were put to very good use. He comfortably assumed command of his dining companions.

"All right, men," The Colonel said. "As per our discussion during the journey here last night, we will break into two units once we reach the police station. Sheriff Carlson and I will interface with Lieutenant Patrick Mullarney, the commanding officer of the Sixty-Eighth Street Police Station, and with Deputy Inspector Michael McDermott. Miller and George will discreetly interview the arresting detectives, Notheis and Clancy, where they will glean information about the arrest, interrogation and the measures that were taken when securing the prisoner's statement. We don't want any surprises when we get into the courtroom. Let's remain flexible, gentlemen, and be ready for anything. Everyone will be debriefed when we return here to the hotel."

After their sumptuous luncheon, the quartet left the hotel and made their way to the Sixty-Eighth Street Police Station by taxi rather than bother with retrieving and re-parking The Colonel's car. When they reached the station, The Colonel and Sheriff Carlson split from the group and sought out the Commanding Officer and the Deputy Inspector. Elmer Miller and Lieutenant George went in search of detectives Clancy and Notheis. They found the detectives in the squad room and befriended them right away. In the middle of their discussion about interrogation policies at the station, a cadet ran into the room and approached Notheis and Clancy.

"Yes, cadet?" said Detective Notheis in a tone that indicated his irritation with the disruption. "What is it? We're having an important meeting here with these two lawmen from Cattaraugus County. They're here to collect that Lindsay character that we collared yesterday."

"Sorry to disturb your conference, sir," the cadet said stridently, "but these gentlemen will be very interested in this news. It's about the vehicle Lindsay stole and drove into the city.

Patrolman Walsh of the Sixty-Eighth reported that it was towed in as an abandoned vehicle on Sunday, March 10. Here's his report, sir."

Detective Notheis took the report from the cadet and sent him on his way. Notheis read it then handed the paper to Elmer Miller, who read it and then handed it to Lieutenant George. The report disclosed that the vehicle had been towed to the police garage, where it remained impounded. The detectives offered to drive Leone Pickup and Lieutenant George to the police garage in an unmarked car so they could determine if the vehicle was, in fact, Bernice Farnsworth's car. The offer was accepted and Lieutenant George asked Detective Clancy to first phone Lieutenant Mullarney's office to inform The Colonel of the latest development.

Meanwhile, The Colonel and Sheriff Carlson were handling the filing of Freddy Lindsay's arrest warrant and interviewing Lieutenant Mullarney and Deputy Inspector McDermott. After speaking with them, The Colonel was satisfied that Freddy's statement had been taken without undue duress. Everything was in order. That is, everything seemed to be in order until they asked if Freddy could be turned over to their custody that evening.

"No," said Lieutenant Mullarney. "I'm afraid it's not such a simple matter here. A judge will have to review the arrest warrant and the prisoner's statement. Then the judge will determine if the man in custody is indeed Alfred Joseph Lindsay. Only then can the prisoner be released to your custody. Given that the court docket is full this afternoon, it will probably be late tomorrow morning or perhaps tomorrow afternoon before Lindsay can be released. I apologize for the inconvenience, Colonel. Things move slowly in a city this size."

"No, no, Lieutenant! No need to apologize. It was naïve of me to think we could be accommodated so quickly. Tomorrow will be fine. After all, Lindsay is not going anywhere, is he?"

The men shared a laugh and wrapped up their conference. Lieutenant Mullarney called down to the desk sergeant and had a cadet sent up to usher The Colonel and Sheriff Carlson to the holding cell so that they could conduct their first interview with Alfred Lindsay. The cadet arrived and led them through a series of doors and hallways, and did not stop until he came to the heavily locked main door of the station jail. He introduced The Colonel and Sheriff Carlson to the guard, who had been notified the two men were on their way. The guard unlocked the door and allowed them to enter. He led them down a corridor lined with small, barred cells containing a wide assortment of criminals. The guard stopped when he reached the cell that held Alfred Lindsay.

Freddy was sitting on the edge of his steel-framed bed; his head was resting on his knees.

"Lindsay!" shouted the guard. "District Attorney Krieger and Sheriff Carlson are here to see you. Get up and face them, now!"

Freddy knew the drill. He was no stranger to harsh treatment from a man with a ring of keys hanging from a brass loop on his belt. He stood up and faced the two strangers standing next to the guard.

"I am the District Attorney and this is the Sheriff," said The Colonel. "We have come to take you back to Cattaraugus County where you will stand trial for the murders of Bernice and Harold Farnsworth. Do you understand what I am saying, Lindsay?"

"Of course, I do," Freddy replied sullenly. "I know why you're here."

"Good! I've read the statement you gave to the detectives and the inspector yesterday. Did you murder Bernice Kenyon?"

"I guess I did if you said I did. I told those detectives and that inspector yesterday that I don't remember anything about Bernice's murder."

"Like I said, Lindsay, I have read your statement and it looks to me as if you said a lot about Bernice's murder. Are you denying now that you said those things?"

"Like I said, sir, I don't remember anything and that's all I have to say right now. I don't remember a thing."

"That's fine. No rush. We will have a lot of time to talk while we make our way back to Little Valley, and even more time after we get you tucked away in jail. We will see you next when you are released into our custody. Good day to you, Mr. Lindsay. Guard, we're done here."

The Colonel made a military left turn and marched back down the corridor with Sheriff Carlson and the guard in tow. They were escorted once again by a cadet who guided them out to the small lobby of the police station. There they waited for forty-five minutes before Elmer Miller and Lieutenant George returned from the police garage with detectives Clancy and Notheis.

After making the necessary introduction of the detectives to The Colonel and Sheriff Carlson, Miller reported that the impounded car was in fact Bernice Farnsworth's 1930 Chevrolet Sport Coupe. He informed them that this was determined when the serial number, motor number, and license plate number all matched exactly with the information acquired from the Department of Motor Vehicles in Little Valley. When Miller finished his brief report, he handed over several sheets of paper that needed to be filled in and signed before the vehicle could be released to the Cattaraugus County Sheriff's Department as evidence in a crime.

The conversation gradually shifted to the roles played by detectives Notheis and Clancy. The men from Cattaraugus County were eager to hear the details surrounding Lindsay's capture and how the detectives got his statement. Just as Inspector McDermott determined earlier in the day, nothing indicated Lindsay had been coerced into signing the statement. Detectives Clancy and Notheis then excused themselves and returned to work.

Colonel Krieger filled out the paperwork in the police station lobby and decided all four men should return to the police garage and file the papers. They hailed a taxi, dropped off the paperwork and arranged for the car to be shipped by rail to Randolph. That left them with nothing to do but wait until a judge saw fit to release Freddy Lindsay into their custody.

The Colonel hailed another taxi and the foursome returned to the hotel where they ordered dinner in a private dining salon and discussed the intelligence each had gathered during the day. Afterwards, they agreed to meet again for breakfast at seven, said good night, and retired for the evening.

Elmer Miller, Lieutenant George, Colonel Krieger, and Sheriff Carlson met up again in the hotel lobby the next morning and headed for breakfast in the dining salon. After they ate, the men found themselves with nothing to do, so they sat in the lobby and read newspapers and magazines. Occasionally, they went out for a walk or a smoke. They checked their watches constantly. The Colonel irritated the front desk clerks with his all-too-frequent trips to the desk to check if a message had come in from Lieutenant Mullarney.

Lunchtime rolled around and it was a welcome distraction. Elmer Miller convinced The Colonel to have their noon meal in a restaurant he had passed on one of his walks. It felt good to be out of the hushed interior of the hotel.

Lunch was a huge success. The Colonel relaxed and for the better part of the hour they forgot about Freddy Lindsay and his release from NYPD custody. They ordered sandwiches, potato chips, and beer all around. Their conversation was spiced by a variety of topics. Miller and Lieutenant George talked about hunting, fishing and local gossip. The Colonel talked about the natural beauty that surrounded his family's summer lodge near Quaker Run. Sheriff Carlson told them that he couldn't wait until the weather warmed enough for a weekend stay at Chautauqua Lake with his wife.

One of them mentioned it was indeed too bad that Deputy Sheriff Leone Pickup was unable to accompany them. The Colonel assured them that the deputy would remain an integral part of the prosecution team. Sheriff Carlson, Elmer Miller and Lieutenant George were pleased to hear this.

The impromptu luncheon served as a catalyst that cemented a bond between the men. They had entered the restaurant as four separate individuals, but left as one cohesive unit. Without realizing it, The Colonel sealed that bond when he demonstrated to the other men that he was as comfortable in their world as he was in his own.

The four men were all poised and ready to bring Freddy Lindsay to trial and then to task for his murderous acts. Although it remained unspoken, each knew he would be instrumental in sending Freddy to his death by electrocution. And, to Freddy's great detriment, not one of them had any reservations about being an integral part of that outcome.

When they returned to the New Yorker Hotel at half-past one, The Colonel again checked for messages at the front desk. He rejoined his companions and informed them that no message had arrived yet from Inspector McDermott. The men groaned and settled back into their lobby chairs.

Elmer Miller and Lieutenant George were bored and began looking for a distraction. Miller asked Lieutenant Carlson if he thought the man at the front desk in the tweed jacket was a duke. They dissected the man's physical characteristics and his body language and decided he was definitely *not* a duke. They switched their attention to a svelte blonde woman engaged in an animated conversation with a group of people across the lobby. She punctuated much of her speech with a sweeping wave of her cigarette holder and an affected laugh. And from there the game continued as other guests entered the lobby. An hour later, a bellboy approached with a message on a tray for The Colonel. The

Colonel picked up the note and replaced it with dollar bill. The bellboy bowed and left.

The message was from Inspector McDermott. He informed The Colonel that the court had approved the transfer of custody and that Alfred Lindsay would be delivered back to the West Sixty-Eighth Street police station by four o'clock that afternoon.

The Colonel asked Elmer Miller, Sheriff Carlson and Lieutenant George for their opinions regarding the best time of day to move Freddy into the Cattaraugus County Jail. Consensus was that early morning hours would be the only time to avoid a mob scene at the jail. The Colonel then called Inspector McDermott and arranged to pick up Freddy at six o'clock that evening.

The four men checked out of the New Yorker Hotel at five-thirty. The Colonel's Cadillac was waiting for them at the curb. They loaded the trunk with their suitcases and got in the car. The Colonel slipped the car into gear and headed for the Sixty-Eighth Street Police Station.

When they arrived, Elmer Miller and Lieutenant George remained in the car while The Colonel and Sheriff Carlson entered the police station. They were met by a cadet and escorted to the station jail to sign out their prisoner.

At 6:20 p.m., The Colonel and Sheriff Carlson emerged with Freddy handcuffed to the sheriff. They loaded Freddy into the backseat first, so that he sat sandwiched between Sheriff Carlson and Elmer Miller. The Colonel got behind the wheel. Lieutenant George was in the front passenger seat.

Once they were all positioned, Sheriff Carlson removed his handcuff and attached it to Elmer Miller to give his own chafed wrist a break. The Colonel started the car and headed north.

They tried to get Freddy to talk on the drive back to Little Valley, but it became obvious that Freddy wasn't going to say anything. They continued the drive in silence and stopped only for gas and food.

The troupe of five tired men arrived in Little Valley at three o'clock in the morning on Thursday, March 14. They escorted Freddy into the county jail, processed him, and walked him down into the basement. Freddy was placed in a cell and The Colonel ceremoniously slammed the cell door shut. The act signaled both the conclusion of Freddy's capture and the beginning of his prosecution for Murder in the First Degree.

CHAPTER SIX

ARRANGEMENTS FOR BERNICE AND HARRY FARNSWORTH'S bodily remains were handled at a dizzying pace. Orla Black called the Coroner's Office on Saturday evening, March 9, 1935, and he spoke with Dr. Marshall L. Hillsman. Hillsman was the surgeon who had performed both autopsies earlier in the day. Orla then spoke with the County Coroner, George A. Middleton, and arranged for the removal of the bodies. The last call he made on Lynn Blessing's behalf was to Fred Meyers at Meyers and Meyers Funeral Home in Randolph. Orla arranged for Meyers to leave immediately for Little Valley to retrieve Bernice and Harold's remains.

The need for speed was required because the couple's bodies had lain in their farmhouse for three and a half days in temperatures that ranged from zero to twenty-two degrees. As a result, the bodies had been frozen and partially thawed two times. As they defrosted in the warmth of the coroner's autopsy room, the decomposition accelerated because their body tissues had been altered during the deep freeze. Embalming the bodies was out of the question. Bernice and Harry needed to be interred as fast as possible before the putrefaction of their flesh advanced any further.

Orla Black called Lynn Blessing at home after speaking with the funeral director. He informed Lynn of the urgency in burying Bernice and Harry no later than the next day. Lynn became agitated again when learning he had to be the bearer of more awful news.

His wife Edith, and her sisters, Morna and Dora, were already at the house on River Street when Lynn received Orla's call. The aftermath of his gruesome announcement regarding immediate burial sent his home into chaos. At first, the three women sat shocked at the task of arranging an immediate funeral service for Bernice. That was followed by concern about the sacrilege of burying Bernice on a Sunday. After a minute or two Dora collapsed and was taken into the parlor where she lay pale and mumbling on the divan. Edith and Morna held each other and cried inconsolably. Lynn ran back and forth between the parlor and the dining room in a futile attempt to care for all three women.

When Edith and Morna unlocked from their embrace, Lynn distracted them by moving them to the parlor to care for Dora. At one point they were so concerned about their sister that they considered calling for the doctor. However, after placing a cool, wet cloth on her forehead, stroking her hand, and talking to her in a reassuring tone, Edith brought Dora around.

Reluctantly, Lynn brought up the subject of Bernice's funeral again. And, although it was not as severe, Edith, Morna and Dora began weeping again.

"All right, ladies!" exclaimed Lynn, "I think I have done enough damage in one day to all of you. I see that I will have to make the decisions here concerning Bernice's funeral. Do any of you have any problem with that?"

As they wiped tears from their eyes with their handkerchiefs, the three women shook their heads from side to side. No, they did not have a problem with Lynn taking over. Lynn called the Meyers Funeral Home and spoke with Fred Meyers' wife, Nina. He arranged for a small private service to be conducted at 2:30 the following afternoon, Sunday, March 10. He asked Nina for the phone number of Reverend Eugene M. Chapman, the rector at the Grace Episcopal Church in Randolph. Then he called the reverend and was relieved when Chapman said he was available Sunday afternoon. The reverend reassured Lynn that he could preside over a Sunday funeral as long as it did not take place on church grounds.

By that time Edith and Morna had calmed down and realized that the phone calls to relatives and friends had to be made by them. They shook off their grief long enough to compile a list of people who needed to be notified about the funeral the next day. One by one they made the necessary calls, apologizing each time for the lateness of the hour and the short notice. To their great relief, no one pressed them about the need to bury Bernice so quickly. Finally, Lynn escorted Morna and Dora home; then he and Edith retired for the night.

Lynn Blessing, Edith, their daughter Olive, and Morna drove to Randolph just past noon the next day. Dora was too ill and too weak to attend Bernice's funeral. Lynn and Edith decided to leave their son, Bobby, in the care of a neighbor.

They arrived at the funeral home, located at 14 Church Street in Randolph, at one o'clock. Edith brought in a fresh dress for Bernice even though she knew it was to be a closed casket service. It was the last act she performed for her beloved sister.

Edith gave the dress to Nina Meyers, entered the small chapel, and sat down in a chair in the front row. Lynn, Morna and Olive joined her. They were inseparable for the rest of the afternoon.

Fred Meyers rolled Bernice's casket out on a bier at 1:30 p.m. Edith began to cry and was immediately followed by Morna and Olive. Lynn felt frustrated because he was unable to ease the grief of the women.

Guests began to arrive at two o'clock. They filed by Lynn, Edith and Morna in a single line that snaked around from the left side of the chapel. Each person murmured a few words of condolence. Some shook hands or hugged. Edith and Morna responded like robots, gracious and polite. To preserve their dignity, they pretended to know nothing of the gossip surrounding Bernice's murder, nor that the rumors were growing more scandalous every day. Robert and Florence Searle were the only people to sit with the family. Six pallbearers assembled and sat directly behind the family. The remainder of the guests sat in neatly arranged rows of chairs behind the pallbearers.

An attempt had been made to contact Harry's family through the police department in Montpelier, Vermont, but they were unable to locate them without more specific information. As a result, no one from Harold Clifford Farnsworth's family was in attendance.

Promptly at 2:30 p.m., Reverend Chapman entered the chapel from a back door and greeted the attendees. He stood in front of Bernice's casket, which lay engulfed in flowers. The flowers had arrived from all over the county. News of the private funeral had spread overnight and somehow people had found flowers to send for a rare, hasty Sunday funeral.

The service was short and no eulogy was given. Immediately after the reverend closed the service, Robert Searle, Raymond Taylor, Leo Terhune, Willard Gibson, Dr. H. B. Hawley, and Lee Armstrong rose from their chairs and filed out of the chapel and into the front of the funeral home. They were followed by the rest of the funeral guests waiting for Bernice's casket to be placed in the first of two hearses parked in the driveway. When her casket was wheeled down the driveway, all six pallbearers grasped the handholds of her casket, hoisted it off the bier, and guided it into the back of the hearse. Harry's casket was loaded into the second hearse.

The two hearses departed for the Randolph Cemetery located nearby at the far end of Main Street. The guests returned to their cars parked on Church Street and they, too, left for the cemetery. The pallbearers moved Bernice and Harry's casket up to two biers set up in front of the two open graves. The gravesites, numbers

280 and 281, were located on the last road at the far back of the cemetery.

Edith and Morna became upset seeing how far away Bernice was to be buried from the Kenyon family plot. But there was no room there for Harry's body so they were forced to purchase the separate plots. This made the two women feel as if they had lost even more of their sister; and their grief scorched their souls. The finality of the open graves had an enormous impact on them. The pain of losing Bernice was palpable.

When the graveside service was over, Lynn needed the assistance of several men to get Edith and Morna to the car. The women sobbed all the way home to Salamanca. Lynn had never felt so helpless in his entire life. There was nothing he could do to console his wife, his daughter, or his sister-in-law.

He dropped Morna off at her house on Broad Street and went in to check on Dora, who remained as she had been that morning. But satisfied that Dora and Morna would be all right alone, he returned to the car and drove Edith home. He put her to bed as soon as they arrived.

Sleep was elusive for every member of the Blessing-Kenyon family that night. The events of the day played over and over in their minds like a sad, endless movie. Edith was finally overcome by exhaustion and fell into a deep sleep early the next morning.

Monday morning came and went without an appearance from Edith. Just as she emerged from their bedroom, late that evening, the phone rang. It was Sheriff Lester Carlson on the other end. He informed Lynn that Freddy Lindsay had been captured in New York City and had made a statement about Bernice and Harry's murder. Carlson promised to update Lynn again when he returned from New York City with Freddy. Surprisingly, Edith took the news very well. More than anything else, she wanted to know what motivated Freddy Lindsay to kill her sister.

At this point, Lynn Blessing's life was occupied with tying

up Bernice's estate. He spent very little time in his studio and had to cancel many lucrative sittings. Most vexing to him was the matter of determining who the heirs were to Bernice and Harold Farnsworth's estate.

Harry's father, Alva Farnsworth, had called the Sheriff's Department in Little Valley after reading a small article about the murder and the manhunt for Alfred Lindsay in a Montpelier newspaper on Tuesday, March 12. The Sheriff's Department referred him to Judge Orla Black.

Alva was very angry when he heard his son had been buried without permission from any Farnsworth family member. Orla Black spent a great deal of time attempting to calm him down.

"Mr. Farnsworth," Orla began, "I understand your anger at having missed the opportunity to say goodbye to your son, Harry, but believe me when I say there was no other choice, sir. Your son's body lay in his home for three and a half days before it was discovered. Without being graphic, may I respectfully say that his body could not have waited for you to arrive. Bernice's family was forced to make the decision to bury your son before your family could be contacted."

When Alva's anger subsided, slowly and methodically Orla convinced Alva to agree to sign off of Harry's estate in exchange for the cost of Harry's burial. He knew that Harry's family could not come up with the money to pay for it. Alva agreed to waive any claim to the Farnsworth estate after Orla promised to send the two-dollar fee for the notary who would verify Alva's signature on the release. Orla felt sorry for the man by the end of their conversation.

When he hung up the phone, Orla instructed his secretary to draw up the necessary papers so that they could be sent out to Alva Farnsworth that very afternoon.

Lynn Blessing was relieved to hear from Orla that the Farnsworths would not prove to be a problem regarding the estate.

There was enough for him to do without having to handle a lengthy and costly lawsuit over Bernice and Harry's meager property. The next hurdle was to determine the value of the estate. He was still waiting for permission from the Sheriff's Department to enter the Farnsworth farmhouse. No one could authorize that entry until Sheriff Carlson returned from New York City with Freddy.

Deputy Sheriff Leone Pickup called Blessing's home at 1:45 p.m. on Thursday, March 14.

"Hello, Lynn!" said Pickup. "Sheriff Carlson asked me to call and give you the good news. Alfred Lindsay was arraigned for Bernice's murder by Justice of the Peace, Rollin Pratt, in Little Valley at one o'clock this afternoon!"

"Thank you for taking the time to call us, Leone. That is great news. Has Lindsay confessed to the murders?"

"Well," hedged Pickup, "yes and no. The Colonel is going to try to get Lindsay to make another statement that will do a better job of incriminating him."

"I see. The Colonel is a keen prosecutor. I'm sure he will have no problem putting this man away."

"Yes, he is, and between you and me, Lynn, The Colonel is going for the death penalty. And I am with him on that one hundred percent. This monster is going to pay with his life for what he did to Bernice!"

"Yes. Absolutely, I agree, Leone. Did the sheriff happen to mention anything about granting me access to Bernice's farmhouse? I have an auction house waiting to gain entry so that everything can be catalogued and hauled off to their warehouse."

"Yes, he did. That was the second reason for my call. Sheriff Carlson says for you to go ahead and empty the house whenever you like. Colonel Krieger and his special investigator are finished with the crime scene."

"Very good, Leone. I will call the auction house as soon as I hang up with you. Thanks again for the phone call. Please keep us informed of The Colonel's progress with this case."

Lynn placed the call to the auction house and arranged to meet them at the farmhouse the next morning, Friday, March 15. He settled back in his easy chair and a bit of satisfaction washed over him. He felt that, at last, he was gaining some control over the chaos that had reigned over his household since they received the news about Bernice's murder. In retrospect, he could scarcely believe that only six days had passed. Lynn fell asleep in his chair and slept deeply.

The moving truck was waiting for Lynn when he arrived at the farmhouse the next morning. He was late because he had become hopelessly lost trying to find the desolate property. He shuddered as he approached the house. The structure looked sinister. He wished he did not have to enter it.

Lynn greeted the crew boss and they organized their work for the day. It was agreed that Lynn would begin in the kitchen and place anything that he did not want taken for auction in the middle of the room. He would do the same in every other room of house while the moving men crated everything else for auction and carried the boxes out to their truck. One man was responsible for cataloging the contents of the truck. He would present Lynn with a tally at the end of the day.

The kitchen and the buttery proved easy and Lynn dispensed with the objects quickly. As he progressed through the dining room to the living room, his sorting slowed. Both rooms contained a lot of correspondence and pictures. Lynn realized that it would be a more efficient use of his time to place all those items in the middle of the room and spend time looking through them later, at home, with Edith.

Lynn had completed the sorting of all objects on the first floor in an hour and a half. The second story was a little harder to get through. Lynn had to search through the strewn clothing that had been ripped out of the dresser drawers. Bernice and Harry's bedroom contained Bernice's personal correspondence and financial records. Interestingly, except for a stack of letters from Bernice, Harry had nothing personal in the house beyond his clothing and shaving gear. Lynn picked up the bundle of letters from Bernice and tossed it into the middle of the room. They landed near a similar pile of letters written from Harry to Bernice.

The basement proved to be the hardest challenge for Lynn. He descended a few cellar stairs and waited for his eyes to adjust to the poor light that entered through the basement windows. Thankfully, when he had descended all the way down, he could not determine where Bernice's body had lain a mere week before. There was nothing in the basement that Lynn wanted to keep. He went back upstairs at eleven o'clock and informed the crew boss that he was done.

Lynn left the house and inspected the barn. As was the case in the basement, there was nothing worth keeping in the barn. He went back to the house through the mudroom.

The crew boss told Lynn that they would be done loading by two o'clock that afternoon. Lynn said he would be back to check on their progress after his lunch in Randolph.

Ira Bennett rode by in his horse and buggy just as Lynn brought his car to a stop at the end of the farm's driveway. He rolled down his window and hailed Ira.

"Say! Hello there!" Lynn called out, "You wouldn't be Ira Bennett would you?"

"Why, yes, sir! I would be him," replied Ira, "Are you Lynn Blessing?"

"Yes, I am," said Lynn as he got out of his car. "You're just the man I wanted to talk to! Have you found any buyers for the livestock yet? We are anxious for them to be sold."

"Yes, as a matter of fact, I have found some buyers," Ira said as he dug in his jacket pocket. "Now, where is that slip of paper? I put it in my pocket before I left. Oh! Here it is! You'll find all of the buyers' names and their offers listed right here. You say the word and they will be here to pick up the animals this weekend."

Lynn looked over the laundry list of animals and the offers for them for a minute and then handed the slip of paper back to Ira.

"Are these fair prices, Ira? I wouldn't know if they were or not. I'm not a farmer."

"Oh, yes, Mr. Blessing," Ira assured Lynn. "They are very fair offers. You're not cuttin' a fat hog on any of the stock, but you aren't getting hurt either. I'd take the offers if it were up to me."

Lynn approved the offers on Ira's say-so and reaffirmed their agreement on Ira's commission for assisting in the care and sale of the livestock. When their business was finished, Lynn continued on to Randolph.

It was 1:30 p.m. before Lynn returned to the farmhouse from Randolph. He found the moving crew waiting for him. They were done packing the items from the house and barn and had finished the inventory list. The list included the estimated value of Bernice and Harold's saleable possessions. Lynn leaned against the fender of his car as he went over the list.

The total estimated value of the articles to be auctioned was set at $153.75. Lynn calculated the total from the livestock offers and reached the sum of $548.75. He sighed with relief. There would be enough to cover the cost of Bernice and Harry's funeral. He went home that afternoon with an enormous load off of his mind.

CHAPTER SEVEN

AT ELEVEN O'CLOCK IN THE MORNING ON THURSDAY, MARCH 14, 1935, Colonel Krieger was asleep in the bedroom of his home in Salamanca. The alarm clock at his bedside startled him as it rang, causing him to bolt upright. He squinted in the semidarkness at the clock's face and remembered that he had to be in Little Valley by 12:30 p.m. He wanted to arrive a half-hour before Alfred Lindsay's arraignment by the Justice of the Peace, scheduled for one o'clock. He showered in the master bathroom, then shaved hastily, nicking himself under his chin. He ripped off a corner of toilet tissue and stuck it to the bleeding nick, cursing the delay it caused.

He dressed quickly and walked out of the bedroom, tightening his tie. He barely acknowledged his wife's presence in the living room and whisked by her in search of his valise. Finding it, he whisked by her again, stooped over and gave her a brushing peck on the cheek. She opened her mouth to speak as he charged out the front door, then shrugged her shoulders and muttered to herself that he was in another of what she called his "focused states."

When The Colonel reached his Cadillac, he jumped in, inserted the key and stomped the starter pedal. The car's powerful engine roared to life and he drove away. He thanked the weather gods for clear weather and the absence of labor-intensive windshield frost.

Exhaustion from lack of sleep clouded The Colonel's brain. He hoped the fog would lift before the arraignment began. He parked at the courthouse in Little Valley and walked to the edge of the downtown area, where he bought a cup of coffee at a luncheonette. He sipped the coffee as he walked back to the courthouse, shifting it from hand to hand when it became too hot to hold. He didn't notice the people gathered on the courthouse lawn.

The Colonel greeted Deputy Sheriff Leone Pickup, who was posted at the entrance to the courthouse. He gave Pickup a curious glance as he watched him unlock the courthouse door that should have been open at this time of day. The Colonel entered the lobby and walked to his ground-floor office. He was relieved that it was only twenty minutes after noon. The coffee began to take its effect and he felt a bit sharper. He took all the paperwork concerning the Lindsay case out of his valise and reviewed it in case Justice Pratt had questions.

It took only a few minutes to familiarize himself with the details of the case. He picked up the nearly empty paper coffee cup and walked to his office window. He had an excellent view of Court Street. He twisted the rod on the venetian blind that covered the window and opened the slats. He froze when he saw what was taking place on the lawn of the courthouse.

The usually serene and unpopulated courthouse lawn had filled with throngs of people in the last few minutes. The Colonel separated two slats of the venetian blind to get a better view. It took a few seconds to register that those people were here for Alfred Lindsay's arraignment. A grin spread across his face in appreciation.

No one but his wife knew that Colonel Krieger aspired to a seat in the county court. He regarded the position of county judge as one of great power and prominence. He was envious of the star treatment that Judge Orla Black received. If he could win election as County Judge, it would be the crowning achievement of his legal career. Standing there and looking down at the crowd of people below, The Colonel knew that a conviction in the Lindsay case might be just the thing to help him win that seat when Orla

Black retired. A shot of adrenaline coursed through him and cleared his head. He was ready to begin the attack on Lindsay and anyone or anything else that stood in his way. The Colonel resolved that he would accept nothing short of sending Alfred Lindsay to the electric chair.

The crowd continued to grow as they massed near the main door to the courthouse. The Colonel rushed to his desk and scooped up the paperwork spread across it. He jammed the papers into his valise and shot out of his office, bounding down the hallway and up the stairs that lead to the courtrooms on the second floor of the building.

Meanwhile, the people outside were pressing forward as they tried to gain admittance to the building. Freddy Lindsay was scheduled to appear in twenty minutes and they wanted to get their seats. Deputy Sheriff Leone Pickup was having a heck of time controlling the crowd. Some of the regular court-attendees complained about the doors to the courthouse being locked. They were used to strolling in and taking a seat in either courtroom without having to go through a barricade or security.

"C'mon," begged one young man. "We got here first! Now let us in, would ya?"

"All of you!" shouted Pickup as he raised one hand, palm facing forward, the other hand resting on his holstered service revolver. "Stop pushing or nobody will get in! Back up! Back up!"

From nowhere, Lynn Blessing squeezed through to the front of the crowd and stood in front of Sheriff Pickup. Pickup recognized him and moved him aside. The mood of the crowd became hostile.

"We won't have to worry about a seat in the courtroom if we go in and yank that woman-killin' bastard out and take care of him ourselves!" shouted someone from the midst of the crowd.

"Whatta ya say, everybody? Should we go in and get him?" shouted another.

The crowd exploded and the rage and disgust that had built up over the past six days spewed out of them.

Shouts of, 'Yeah! Let's go get him!' and 'I say we hang the son of a bitch right here!' rang out. Suddenly, like a ripple in water, the crowd surged forward towards Pickup. This act forced him to draw his weapon.

Lynn Blessing reacted in a way he had never done before. Rather than avoid the conflict, he got angrier than hell and entered the fray. The anger he had suppressed surrounding Bernice and her circumstances surfaced and it energized him. Without realizing what he was doing, he yelled out in a thundering voice that rang out over the din of the crowd.

"Stop, I say! Stop! All of you!" he shouted, holding up his hand to the crowd.

Lynn caught the attention of those closest to him and they stopped surging forward in order to listen. The crowd behind them was held temporarily at bay.

"Most of you here today should know me," he said when he had their attention. "I'm Lynn Blessing. Chances are I have photographed you and probably most of your relatives at one time or another. What you may not know is that I am the brother-in-law of Bernice Kenyon. And on her behalf and on behalf of her immediate family I implore you to let the wheels of justice roll on here. That is what Bernice, as an officer of this court, would want. This man, Alfred Lindsay, isn't going to go free! I guarantee it. Twelve of our good men will be sitting in judgment of him very soon. And I know that they will not let a guilty man go free! Now, please, calm down! Calm down and back away. Let's not have the world think we're a bunch of lawless rural vigilantes. Thank you. That's all I have to say."

Lynn turned and looked at Sheriff Pickup. Pickup unlocked the main door and let Lynn Blessing enter the building.

Lynn's outburst had its desired effect. People murmured, but no longer shouted or pushed towards the door. Lynn restored the peace in forty-five seconds. Sheriff Pickup placed his revolver back in its holster and took control of the crowd at the door. He told people in front to pass the word back through the crowd that he would begin to let them into the courthouse in a few minutes.

Pickup was nervous as he turned his back to unlock the door. He opened one door and the crowd filed in one-by one until Pickup reasoned that the maximum number of seats in the courtroom had been filled. He halted the progression of the line and again told the people in front to pass down the information that he would allow them into the lobby once the arraignment began. The once unruly crowd begrudgingly accepted that they would not be able to sit in the courtroom. Most of them were content, figuring they could tell their friends and neighbors they were there. It was obvious to Leone Pickup that the crowd scene would worsen during the course of the trial.

Upstairs, Freddy Lindsay was led into the courtroom, shuffling, bound in leg irons. He was surrounded by three deputies and a bailiff. No one was taking any chances. Sheriff Carlson was determined to keep control over his high-profile prisoner. Already there was talk among the sheriff's staff that Freddy's gangster brother, Robert Lindsay, might be on his way to Little Valley to break him out of jail.

The Colonel barely acknowledged Freddy's entrance. Instead, he focused on the paperwork in front of him. At exactly one o'clock, the bailiff asked the courtroom to rise for Justice Rollins as he entered the courtroom and took the bench. Many court regulars murmured their surprise at seeing Justice Rollins instead of Orla Black. They were unaware that Orla had recused himself from any case that involved Bernice Kenyon Farnsworth.

Orla Black knew that any decision he oversaw in the courtroom for the criminal case, and any matter brought before the Surrogate Court on the behalf of Bernice's estate could be easily overturned on appeal. He and Bernice had worked together far too long for him to be considered capable of rendering an impartial decision. Justice Rollins was a temporary replacement until Colonel Krieger could find a suitable judge for the case.

Justice Rollins made short work of Freddy's arraignment. It required only a few minutes for him to consider the merit of the charges brought before him against the defendant. Even though the law required a mandatory Not Guilty plea in cases involving capital crimes, he asked Freddy Lindsay for his plea to the charge as a formality. Freddy replied in a weak, timid voice, and his Not Guilty plea was recorded by the court stenographer. Rollins instructed Colonel Krieger to see that a grand jury was impaneled for the sole purpose of indicting Alfred Lindsay for the charge of Murder in the First Degree. This was done in accordance with the Fifth Amendment to the United States Constitution. The amendment requires that charges for all capital and "infamous" crimes be brought by an indictment returned by a grand jury. After he remanded Freddy to the custody of the county sheriff, he banged his gavel sharply and recessed the court.

The deputies, who had been standing to the side and behind Freddy while he sat at the defendant's table, hoisted him up by his armpits and dragged him out of the courtroom. The crowd waited until Freddy was gone before they got up and left.

The bailiff ran to the stairs ahead of the spectators and on the landing above the lobby he announced that Alfred Lindsay had been arraigned and had pleaded not guilty. The crowd roared with approval.

The noise of the crowd filtered through the heavy courtroom doors where The Colonel was still seated at the prosecutor's table. For the second time in less than hour, a smile spread across his face as he listened to their voices. To anyone who might be paying attention, he looked like the cat that ate the canary.

When the crowd dispersed, The Colonel went downstairs to

the County Clerk's Office. Guy Fargo was at his desk. The Colonel instructed Fargo to impanel a grand jury for the sole purpose of indicting Alfred J. Lindsay for the capital offense of First Degree Murder. After making a few adjustments to the court calendar, Guy assured him that the grand jury could meet on Wednesday, March 20.

Colonel Krieger spent the rest of the afternoon cloistered in his office with Special Investigator Elmer Miller, Sheriff Carlson and State Trooper Lieutenant George. The men pored over all the statements The Colonel and Deputy Sheriff Pickup had amassed from witnesses before The Colonel had left for New York City last Monday evening. They were trying to ascertain which witnesses should be subpoenaed to give testimony to the grand jury.

The grand jury witness list was finalized by five o'clock that afternoon. The list was short and sweet. The Colonel would be calling Sheriff Carlson, Ira Bennett, Nora Moynihan, Doctor Marshall Hillsman, Fred Houlihan and Leone Pickup to testify. The Colonel limited the number of witnesses because he wanted all the testimony to take place in a single day. He was hoping to conduct the trial and get a conviction by the second week in April.

As a backup, The Colonel decided to draw up a second list of witnesses that might be helpful in case they ran into trouble with the grand jury. With help from Miller, Carlson and Lieutenant George, he developed a list of eight more individuals. They included Jay Stevens, Leland Burr, Truman Colburn, William Frary, John Monroe, Robert Deppa and Leon Johnson. He told Sheriff Carlson that the subpoenas for all the witnesses would be ready to pick up at his office tomorrow afternoon. Sheriff Carlson would then see that the subpoenas were duly served on each of the prospective witnesses by Deputy Sheriff Pickup.

Carlson, Miller, and Lieutenant George agreed to stay and assist The Colonel in interviewing Freddy in his office later that evening in order to obtain a better statement from him. The Colonel placed a call to the secretarial pool and requested that a stenographer be available at seven o'clock to record the meeting. All four men left the building at half-past five and had dinner at a restaurant in downtown Little Valley.

They returned to The Colonel's office at 6:45 p.m. and he gave the men a brief lecture about interrogation procedures and explained their roles. He was also especially clear that everything was to be done strictly by the book. The Colonel emphasized that the trial would be fair and cleanly run, from pre-trial to verdict.

When The Colonel finished his instructions, Sheriff Carlson went to the jail to retrieve Freddy. He returned at 7:25 with two deputies who were posted outside the door to The Colonel's office. The men made small talk with Freddy until the stenographer, Frances W. Chambers, arrived with her steno machine at 7:35. She set up her equipment and was ready to start recording at 7:45.

The Colonel was a meticulous man. Once he set himself to task he maintained a slow and steady pace that never wavered from its pre-ordained destination. He was adept at building monuments from a staggering collection of tiny components. And he was often compared to a steamroller. When Colonel Krieger came up to speed, he was unstoppable. By utilizing his persona and sheer will, he was able to flatten everything in his path. The Colonel made a subtle shift into steamroller mode and began the interview with Freddy Lindsay.

Freddy was first asked simple, personal questions, ending with his current age. Then The Colonel abruptly shifted to questions about how, when and where he had met Harold Farnsworth. He moved on to questions about what Freddy had learned about Bernice while he and Harold were incarcerated at Great Meadow Prison in Comstock, New York. Freddy insisted he had not known anything about Bernice other than that she was a girl to whom Harold wrote a lot of letters. Then The Colonel focused on Freddy's criminal record.

The rest of the interview bobbed and weaved wildly through many topics. The Colonel hoped to catch Freddy in a lie by shifting the focus of his interrogation. This went on for quite a while, until he was ready to begin his serious questioning regarding how the murders took place. The Colonel was surprised at how cooperative Freddy was, except that he didn't remember swinging an axe over Bernice's body. Freddy claimed to draw a blank from the moment he hit Bernice with the flat of the axe until he found himself upstairs struggling with Harry. No amount of badgering could budge him.

They took a fifteen-minute break at nine o'clock and then The Colonel picked up exactly where he had left off. Freddy complained he had a headache and Lieutenant George was sent out to get him an acetidine. The interrogation lasted until 10:15 and The Colonel felt that he had gotten all he could from Freddy. He instructed Frances Chambers, the stenographer, to transcribe the interview and to provide him with two copies. The others took another break as they waited for the transcription.

Frances returned forty-five minutes later with two copies of the eighty-two page transcription. The Colonel got right back to work and discussed specific responses with Freddy. He circled every statement that Freddy agreed was correct. The process of cobbling together Freddy's statement from the interview transcript took another twenty-five minutes. Then The Colonel dictated the circled statements to Frances, who recorded it all on her steno machine. Freddy listened, and at the end of The Colonel's dictation said that it sounded good to him.

Frances immediately went to work on the dictated statement and produced a transcript in fifteen minutes. Freddy read it over carefully and made several corrections in his own handwriting. Frances retyped the pages, incorporating the corrections, and by

12:15 on the morning on Friday, March 15, Freddy had signed all six pages of the statement. Sheriff Carlson, Elmer Miller and Lieutenant George then placed their signatures in the margin of the document as witnesses. The Colonel thanked the three men and the stenographer for staying so late and announced they were done for the night.

Sheriff Carlson bade each one of the other men goodnight as he collected Lindsay, re-attached the leg irons and escorted the prisoner out of The Colonel's office. Frances Chambers and Elmer Miller left first and were soon followed by Colonel Krieger and Lieutenant George.

By the time The Colonel was halfway home, the toll of the long hours without sufficient rest caught up with him. He had to fight to stay awake, but mercifully he made it home safely and fell asleep as soon as his head hit the pillow. It would not be the last time he arrived home in that state. The Colonel's work on behalf of the State of New York versus Alfred Joseph Lindsay had just begun.

CHAPTER EIGHT

THE MORNING OF FRIDAY, MARCH 15, 1935 WAS A BUSY ONE FOR the secretarial pool at the Cattaraugus County Clerk's office. Every available secretary was busy preparing the summonses for the grand jurors as well as the summonses for the witnesses who were scheduled to testify in front of them. Deputy Sheriff Leone Pickup impatiently paced back and forth outside the clerk's office. He was anxious to begin the long process of summons delivery for the members of the grand jury. The Colonel and Sheriff Carlson insisted that each of the summonses for the grand jury members and witnesses be delivered by Pickup and no one else. They were confident that the more experienced deputy would serve each summon in accordance with the requirements for legal service as set forth by law.

The grand jury consisted of twenty-three members who hailed from cities all across the county. The jury foreman was Ray Moran of Olean. The assistant foreman was Lewis N. Land of Olean. The rest of the jury consisted of the following people: Peter Elling of Olean, U. S. Mosher of Portville, Arthur Hall of Perrysburg, J. C. Willover of Hinsdale, Floyd Scott of Ashford, Walter Dolph of Salamanca, Howard Boyer of Red House, Walter Neal of Salamanca, Charles Metzler of Salamanca, Christ Kammire of Salamanca, Ed Norton of Salamanca, Eugene Cricks of Salamanca, J. H. Young of Ellicottville, Lewis Slocum of Salamanca, James Maley of Salamanca, Alvin Dechow of New Albion, Bert Barton of Conewango, Godfrey Berne of South Valley, Paul Cain of Elko, Edward Mooney of Olean, and Albert Reitz of Alleghany.

Leone Pickup was waiting for the twenty-three grand jury summonses and an additional fourteen witness summonses, bringing the total served to thirty-seven. It was a staggering amount for him to deliver, especially at this time of the year when the weather significantly slowed travel.

To complicate matters, the secretarial pool was also drawing up summonses for another case to be presented to the grand jury on the same day, Wednesday, March 20. In addition, the State was asking for an indictment to be brought against Gilbert Lafay of East Otto for first-degree assault.

Leone Pickup did not receive his summonses until well after eleven o'clock in the morning. He sorted the summonses by area and left immediately in his car to begin delivery. He began with the summonses for Salamanca, as they were the closest to the courthouse.

The process of serving individual summonses proved to be laboriously slow. Many of the jurors were at work and Pickup had to track down each one. Often he arrived at the correct address but found no one at home. But Pickup persevered and delivered a good portion of the Salamanca summonses before five o'clock. After that, his rate of success climbed and he was able to deliver all of the Salamanca summonses by the end of the evening.

Pickup left his home at nine o'clock the following morning, Saturday, March 16, and began delivering the rest of the grand jury summonses. He delivered the last one at six o'clock that evening. He then returned home and did not attempt to deliver any of the witness summonses on Sunday, March 17.

Deputy Sheriff Pickup delivered the remainder of the witness summonses on March 18, with the exception of the papers for Robert Deppa and Leon Johnson of Randolph. To save time and give those witnesses as much notice as possible, Sheriff Carlson agreed to have them served by Deputy Arrowsmith late Monday evening.

While Pickup was out serving summonses, The Colonel was busy firing off letters of inquiry. On Friday, he dictated letters to the prison wardens at Great Meadow, Sing Sing, and Auburn Penitentiary requesting information regarding Harry Farnsworth and Freddy Lindsay while they were incarcerated in those prisons. Then he dictated a letter to J. Edgar Hoover at the Federal Bureau of Investigation asking for a complete arrest record for Alfred Joseph Lindsay.

The list of persons to be contacted was enormous. It included other law enforcement agencies, psychologists, forensic testing laboratories and various federal and state agencies. The Colonel completed letters to half the people on his list by five o'clock Friday afternoon. He brought in a secretary on Saturday, March 16 and spent most of the day dictating letters. They finished by mid-afternoon and he found himself affixing his signature to a formidable stack of letters at five o'clock. The Colonel left his office in the courthouse at six o'clock on Saturday evening and did not return until nine o'clock on the morning of Monday, March 18.

Next door at the Sheriff's Office, Sheriff Lester Carlson was still trying to cope with the stress of housing a high-profile prisoner. He had gotten phone calls from every high-ranking county official regarding the security at the county jail. The sheriff had long considered the installation of yard lights around the building, so he called the county maintenance division and ordered the procurement and installation of three yard lights for the jailhouse.

Then Carlson placed a call to Lieutenant George at the Friendship State Troopers Post. He wasted no time getting to the point.

"Hello, Lieutenant George! Sheriff Carlson calling. I need a big favor if you can deliver it."

"Well, I will try my best to help you, Sheriff," Lieutenant George replied.

"Very good, then! I've got my hands full here with this Lindsay fellow and it's proving to be a big strain on my employees here. There has been some talk about Lindsay's brother coming up here to Little Valley with his gang to break his brother out of jail. Now, I'm not saying that this is the case, mind you, but I am suggesting that it might possibly be true. I think it would be prudent to position a few sharpshooters on the roof of the jail for a few days just in case. And I thought that the National Guard in Olean might be the place to obtain those sharpshooters. Do you hold any sway over the National Guard in Olean, Lieutenant?"

"Hmmm. I never thought about the brother coming up to bust Lindsay out of jail. And, yes, I do have a good rapport with the commanding officer at the National Guard and have worked with him on several cases. I would be happy to give him a call and see what I can do on your behalf. I'll have him call you back."

"Thank you, Lieutenant. And, please, feel free to call on us whenever my office can be of assistance to you."

The commanding officer at the Olean National Guard called Sheriff Carlson a few hours later and agreed to provide him with four sharpshooters. The sharpshooters arrived at six o'clock that evening and were positioned on the roof of the jail, one pair at a time, in shifts of twelve hours each. By positioning each sharpshooter at opposite corners of the roof, they were able to provide coverage of a three-hundred-sixty-degree circle around the jailhouse.

The yard lights were installed on Tuesday, March 19, and were switched on for nighttime use at 6:30 that evening. The residents who lived nearby were not happy with the new lights and complaints came in as soon as darkness fell in Little Valley. The lights were re-positioned to accommodate the residents and there was no further problem with them. The mood at the jail improved markedly after the yard lights went into service.

Sheriff Carlson completed his security plan by placing

Freddy in the furthermost cell on the third floor of the jailhouse. He placed two guards at Freddy's cell door and ordered that Freddy could not use metal eating utensils, that all his meals would need to be prepared on the third floor, and that no item, under any circumstances, was to be allowed onto the third floor without his prior approval. Sheriff Carlson went home Tuesday evening feeling quite confident that his prisoner was secure. The night came and went without incident.

The members of the grand jury began to arrive at the courthouse at half-past eight the morning of Wednesday, March 20. Deputy Nix was posted at the courtroom door and checked off their names from his list as they entered. The witnesses assembled in the hallway outside the courtroom. The Colonel showed up at 8:50 and sat at the prosecutor's table. When the courthouse clock struck nine o'clock, everyone was present and accounted for inside and outside the courtroom. Grand jury foreman Ray Moran convened the grand jury and turned the floor over to The Colonel.

The first person called to testify was Sheriff Carlson. The bailiff went to the courtroom door, opened it and leaned out. He called out the sheriff's name and ushered him to the witness chair situated between the judge's bench and the jury box. Before the sheriff took his seat, he placed his hand on a bible and was sworn in. The grand jury members observed the proceedings from front row chairs in the audience section. The rest of the audience section was empty. All grand jury proceedings were held in secret.

The examination of Sheriff Carlson was done by the book. The sheriff's identity was established. He testified about the facts surrounding the murder. He described the Farnsworth's farmhouse and where it was located. Sometimes he referred to a hand-drawn diagram of the Farnsworth house and their barn. He provided the identities of all the men at the crime scene when he had arrived at the Farnsworth farmhouse on Friday, March 8.

The Colonel introduced a set of photographs taken by

Sylvester Nodler and Walter Wilhelm. He asked Sheriff Carlson to identify the bodies in two of the photos. He also identified the axe in a photo of the basement. The Colonel then shifted to Sheriff Carlson's trip to New York City on March 12. Through questioning, Carlson clearly laid out Lindsay's arrest in New York and the process whereby he was turned over for return to Cattaraugus County.

"Was any force or duress or threats of any kind used to get him to make a statement to you?" The Colonel asked.

Sheriff Carlson replied, "No."

"You talked with him not only about the murders, but about his former life and places he had been. The two of you talked very casually?"

"Yes."

"You may state the substance of any statement that he made to you in reference to whether or not he was the man who killed Mr. and Mrs. Farnsworth."

"Why, he said he had killed them both!"

The examination continued and Carlson stated that Freddy claimed to have hit Bernice once by accident and that he took the gun away from Harold who was about to shoot him. The sheriff also testified that Freddy admitted to shooting Harold three times.

Eventually the examination steered from the sheriff to the topic of his witnessing of Bernice's autopsy. This shift gave The Colonel an opportunity to introduce the extent of Bernice and Harold's wounds to the grand jury. Sheriff Carlson was excused from the stand when he finished testifying about the condition of the bodies on the coroner's autopsy table.

Ira Bennett was called next. After the obligatory testimony that identified Ira and his close proximity to the farm, he testified about the sale of the McGraw Farm to Bernice and Harold Farnsworth in September of the previous year. He established that the farm was isolated and that the nearest neighbor was a mile away. He also established that he last saw the Farnsworths at his farm on Monday, March 4, in the afternoon when he talked to Harry about the return of the wood rack. The Colonel continued establishing small details that would be useful to him later.

The line of questioning changed abruptly to the events that took place on the day that Ira Bennett and William Whitmore discovered the bodies at the Farnsworth farm. Ira described the condition of the barn and the livestock. He moved on to the discovery of Harry's body on the living room floor, and then to the condition of the bedrooms upstairs. The Colonel showed photographs of Harry lying on the floor and Ira agreed that everything in the photo was exactly as he had seen it when he discovered the body.

Ira testified about his phone call to the home of Deputy Sheriff Leone Pickup and the conversation he had with the sheriff's wife. His testimony ended with the time of the arrival of Deputy Sheriff Pickup and Lieutenant George at the farm.

The next witness called to testify was Nora Moynihan. She was upset and nervous. Sensing this, The Colonel modulated his voice and took a softer stance. He established her identity and her relationship with Bernice Farnsworth as a neighbor of four years. Then he established that Nora first met Freddy Lindsay in February of this year. Nora testified about her experience with Freddy while visiting the Farnsworths at their house a week before the murders.

"Do you know of any trouble between Lindsay and the Farnsworths?" The Colonel asked.

"Yes," Nora Moynihan replied.

"You may state any trouble you know of between them."

"They came to my place after bread and apple pie on the twenty-fourth of February. It was the day my parents were married and he sat around in a grouch all that time."

"Lindsay?"

"Yes, all that afternoon he didn't talk much. We arrived there at one o'clock and I told them I had to go back home about four o'clock. When Lindsay and Farnsworth went to the barn I asked Bernice if Freddy sat in a grouch like that all of the time. She said he had for three or four days, and I asked her if it didn't get on her nerves. She said it does, and I said, 'I would call that a mental case!' She said she did, too."

Then The Colonel established that Nora had seen the Farnsworths on Monday, March 4, in the late afternoon, and that she saw Harry Farnsworth travel to and from the milk plant making his usual morning milk run on Tuesday. The Colonel asked Nora about Freddy Lindsay's appearance at her farm on Monday afternoon before he headed to Steamburg, and to explain what happened when the Farnsworth stopped by a little later looking for Freddy. Slowly, Nora lost her ability to focus on the questions. She offered more information than was asked or provided information beyond the scope of the question he put forth to her.

The Colonel decided to humor Nora when she wandered and brought her back to the point of each question when it was not properly answered. He was particularly annoyed, however, when out of the blue Nora, began to accuse Freddy Lindsay of stealing a pair of gloves and wearing them when he was arrested. She even went so far as to produce the empty glove box from her purse. The Colonel took the glove box from her and set it aside.

He wrapped up Nora Moynihan's testimony by getting her to identify the abandoned house that Freddy Lindsay slept in the night before the murders. He also established that Freddy had stolen the keys to her brother's house from her.

Dr. Marshall Hillsman, the coroner's surgeon, took the stand next. He described the wounds on each of the bodies and their exact locations. Through a series of questions, it was established that the blow to the neck that partially severed Bernice's head was the killing wound. It was his belief that Bernice was unconscious when the blow was delivered.

Dr. Hillsman described Harry's wounds and identified the gunshot wound to the left base of the skull as the shot that killed him instantly. He described the damage done to Harry's brain tissue by the bullet, and the bone it shattered before entering his brain.

"Following the track in the soft tissue of the brain... following the track of this bullet for an area of, I would say, an inch in diameter, the brain was mushed after bone and lead went through it. This bullet had gone through the brain and ended up lodged on the right side of the base of the skull on the inside of it."

The Doctor gave his opinion as to the type of weapon used to kill Bernice Farnsworth and how it was employed by her murderer. He gave his opinion on Freddy Lindsay's version of how the murders occurred. He said Freddy's version was conceivable but very improbable.

One of the jurors interrupted The Colonel to ask the purpose of Dr. Hillsman's examination of Freddy Lindsay on March 14 upon his arrival at the jailhouse. The interjection unnerved The Colonel, who was always annoyed when interrupted during a line of questioning. However, this was a grand jury session and not a trial. Questions from the jurors were allowed.

Dr. Hillsman answered the juror by stating that he had been looking for evidence of a struggle on Lindsay's body, but had found none. The Colonel returned to questioning the doctor who, at the end of his testimony, stated he was unsure if there was one blow or two to Bernice's neck. The doctor was excused.

The grand jury foreman asked for a brief recess and everyone took a twenty-minute break. When they returned and reconvened the session, The Colonel called for Fred Houlihan, owner of Houlihan's Garage in Steamburg, to take the stand.

Fred's testimony was short. He stated he had never seen any

trouble between Harry Farnsworth and Freddy Lindsay, although he saw them often in his garage. He testified about Freddy's arrival at his garage on Monday afternoon, March 4, and the arrival of Bernice and Harold Farnsworth later. His testimony ended with Bernice and Harry disappearing over the hill and Freddy trudging down the highway in the same direction.

Deputy Sheriff Leone Pickup was called next. Pickup testified he had been the first officer to arrive on the scene with Lieutenant George. He chronicled the arrival of Coroner Middleton and the four deputies that accompanied the coroner. He was questioned about the investigation of the abandoned house that Lindsay spent the night in on March 4. Pickup described the items he found there and noted that the electricity was working in the house. He also stated that some of the items Nora Moynihan reported as stolen from her by Lindsay were found in the abandoned house.

Pickup's testimony ended after he described the condition of the upstairs bedrooms at the farmhouse and the discovery of the pried-open cashbox.

The Colonel concluded his presentation of evidence against Freddy by reading the statement that Freddy Lindsay made after he arrived back in Cattaraugus County. The grand jury had a few questions for The Colonel and then they adjourned for lunch.

After lunch, the grand jury heard the evidence presented by The Colonel in a case against Gilbert Lafay. Several witnesses took the stand and the Lafay case was completed by 3:30 that afternoon. The grand jury recessed to take both cases under consideration.

The phone on The Colonel's desk rang just before five o'clock. It was the grand jury foreman, Ray Moran, on the other end of the line. He said that the grand jury had returned with an indictment of First Degree Murder for Alfred J. Lindsay.

The Colonel dashed across the courthouse lobby to give the

news of the indictment to Guy Fargo in the County Clerk's office. After considering all the cases on the docket for April, Fargo set a date for Freddy Lindsay's trial. Jury selection would begin on Monday, April 1. The Colonel left the clerk's office and ran to the telegraph office a few blocks away in downtown Little Valley. He sent a telegram to the newsroom at the Jamestown *Post*. The telegram read, "Lindsay trial is on—April 1."

Afterwards, The Colonel returned to his office to place a call to Judge George Larkin. He explained the state's predicament with each of the judges that currently heard cases in the county courthouse. Judge Larkin agreed there was not a judge in the county or on the circuit who could be impartial when overseeing a trial for Bernice Farnsworth's murder. Even still, Larkin balked when The Colonel asked him to come out of semi-retirement and hear the case. The judge argued that he, too, had spent a considerable amount of time with Bernice in the courtroom. The Colonel countered that it had been many years since they had worked together and that they had very little contact with one another after the election of Orla Black many years ago. Reluctantly, the judge agreed to hear the case.

Judge Larkin's first act as judge for the case was to appoint an attorney for Freddy Lindsay since he could not afford one for himself. The custom of the court at that time was to appoint the top litigator in the court's jurisdiction to handle the defense in cases where capital punishment was at stake. The choice for defense counsel in this case was simple. Judge Larkin called G. Sydney Shane at his law office in Salamanca and left word that Mr. Shane was to take over the Lindsay case. He suggested Shane should meet with his new client that evening.

Then Judge Larkin called Cornelius J. McCarthy. He wanted McCarthy to assist Syd Shane as his co-counsel. He left a message for McCarthy to meet with his new partner, and left Shane's name and phone number.

The graying Judge leaned back in his chair at his desk in his home office and thought back to the day he talked Bernice into returning to the courtroom. It stuck him as odd to think that if hadn't interfered back then, she would more than likely still be alive. Remembering her utter loneliness that day, he reasoned that she might never have known love if she hadn't met Harry Farnsworth in that courtroom back in 1929. He left it at that.

Syd Shane picked up the message about his appointment as Freddy Lindsay's counsel at seven o'clock that evening. It surprised him to learn that he had drawn the case, but he decided to go to the county jail and meet with his client right away. He walked over to the coat rack in the empty reception room of his office, donned his fedora, and slipped on a tan overcoat.

He arrived at the county jail at 7:45 p.m. He stopped at the sheriff's office and introduced himself to the night deputy in charge. The deputy walked him over to the jail, led him to a small reception area and left. Another deputy greeted Shane and escorted him to the third floor of the jailhouse. Syd was surprised to see so many deputies posted at key locations inside the jailhouse.

Finally, Shane entered the long hallway that led down past a row of cells. Two deputies were standing in front of the cell farthest away from him. He walked up to the cell and motioned with his hands for the guards to separate so that he could see behind them. The guards moved aside, revealing Freddy Lindsay sitting on his bunk with his feet spread apart and his head hanging down. He did not acknowledge Syd's presence.

"Are you Alfred Lindsay?" asked defense counsel Syd Shane.

"No. I'm Freddy Lindsay."

"Ok, then. Freddy it is," Shane said with a smile as he extended his right hand through the bars on the cell. "Pleased to meet you. I'm Syd Shane and I am your attorney."

Freddy turned his head and looked up at Shane. He ignored the attorney's extended hand and looked him squarely in the eye. Shaking his head slightly from side-to-side, Freddy said, "You poor bastard."

CHAPTER NINE

GEORGE SYDNEY SHANE WAS BORN ON VALENTINE'S DAY, February 14, 1902, to Frederick and Margaret Riley Shane in Toledo, Ohio. Frederick Shane had recently moved to Toledo with his wife from Corning, New York, where he had been employed as a glass blower at the Corning Glass Works. The glass works had been immobilized due to a protracted strike by workers there who wanted to join the Glass Blowers Union. Frederick Shane had quit right after the owners of the glass works publically announced that they would rather shutter their business than agree to the unionization of their employees. Frederick went to Toledo and obtained employment at a glass factory there operated by Libby-Owens.

In the course of his stay in Toledo, Frederick became involved in the Democratic Party. He moved up the Democratic political ladder quickly and one day found himself being groomed as a candidate for the U.S. Senate. One evening, he left on a boat with twelve high-ranking Democratic Party officials to discuss his candidacy for the senate seat. A bomb exploded on board the boat shortly after it left the dock. Everyone on board was killed. Although it was never proved, many blamed the deaths on rival politicians.

Margaret Shane had no choice but to move back to Corning to support her child. She eventually remarried and raised Syd with her new husband, Louis Terbrack. Syd was an excellent student through the primary grades and attended high school and two years of college-level work at the well-respected Saint Bonaventure School. He transferred to the University of Buffalo where he received a law degree and easily passed the New York bar exam in 1924.

G. Sydney Shane landed his first job with an insurance company in Buffalo as a claims agent. Standard practice at the time was to hire newly minted attorneys to settle claims made against the company. Shane would be given two or three thousand dollars in cash and sent out to settle claims with people who, for instance, were injured while working for the railroad or while traveling on a trolley that tipped over when the horse that pulled it bucked out of control. When cash was wiggled under their noses, many people signed off for a few hundred dollars on claims that should have been compensated at a much higher rate. Syd hated the job and quickly began looking for another opportunity where he could practice the skills he had learned at the university.

The opportunity came one day while scanning the want ads in a Buffalo newspaper. Thomas Dowd, a rare democratic judge in Cattaraugus County, was advertising for junior attorneys to practice in his law office in Salamanca. Since the town was so close to where Syd had grown up, he applied for the job, figuring he knew the territory and he might do well there. Dowd hired him immediately.

Syd Shane's role in personal injury lawsuits against the railroads changed significantly while practicing at the Dowd office. Due to federal legislation, railroad workers had won the right to sue their employees for any injury that occurred as a result of their employment. Shane was assigned to their cases and took full advantage of the new legislation. Within a short time, he had gained a reputation as a keen litigator able to get big money from the much-hated railroad barons to compensate the common people for their injuries.

It was inevitable that Syd Shane would break away from the Dowd firm and opened his own office in the Dowd building. His reputation soared and his new office was very successful. It was at this point in his career that Syd Shane was chosen to defend Alfred Lindsay.

Freddy's response of 'you poor bastard,' after Shane introduced himself that night at the county jail, shocked Shane. But just then, the doorway at the end of the hallway clanged open and Shane saw a large, good-looking man in an expensive suit being led towards him by a deputy.

"Hello!" said the man. "I'm looking for G. Sydney Shane."

"That would be me, sir," Shane replied with a grin. "Are you by any chance Cornelius J. McCarthy?"

"Yes, that's me, all right!"

"Well, that's quite a name you have there, Mr. McCarthy. I'll bet your friends call you Corny for short, eh?" Shane said, teasing.

"No," said McCarthy, who was visibly dismayed by Shane's remark. "My friends call me Mac."

Realizing that he had unintentionally insulted the man, Shane grinned again and stuck out his right hand. "Good enough then, Mac. My friends call me Syd."

McCarthy softened and smiled. He grasped Shane's hand and shook it vigorously.

"Let me introduce you to our client, Mr. Freddy Lindsay. Freddy was just telling me that I was a poor bastard for having drawn his case. Isn't that right, Freddy?"

"Yep. You got your work cut out with me, I'll tell ya!"

"Why don't we three talk about that, Freddy? Mac and I have been assigned to your case by the court. We're going to need to talk with you extensively in order to prepare your case for trial. I think now is a good time to get started. What about you? Shall we begin?"

"Nothin' to talk about as far as I'm concerned. Read the statement I gave to the DA and you'll know everything there is to know about me and the murders."

"No, you don't understand. We have to work up a strategy for your defense. Do you realize that you became eligible for the death penalty when the grand jury indicted you on two very serious murder charges today?"

"Yep. I know all right. I've been waiting for it to happen. I knew it would happen right after I left Harry and Bernice's farm. Sometimes, when I close my eyes or when I try to fall asleep, I see Old Sparky. He's just sittin' there with his straps hanging wide open, waiting to wrap around my arms and legs. All ready to pin me down. There's nothin' you two can do about it. It's gonna happen."

Freddy's statement sent chills down Shane's spine. "Now wait a minute, Freddy! I'm not so sure you are guilty of anything more than second-degree murder. Did you go to their farm with the intent to rob or kill that couple?"

"No. I went to collect the money they owed me. The welchers owed me money and I wanted them to pay me before I left for my sister's in New Rochelle."

"Well, in that case, Freddy, you can't be guilty of either of these charges. The murder of that couple was not premeditated and it is not connected with any other crime. Let's get started on your defense, shall we?"

"I've got nothin' to say. Like I already told ya, read my statement. That's all I know."

Shane shoved his fedora back on his head and scratched his scalp as he stared at Freddy in disbelief. "Okay," said Shane, "but that doesn't stop me and my partner Mac here from doing something on your behalf. Freddy, are you sure you don't want to participate in your defense?"

"Nope. Nothin' I can do and nothin' I can say will change anything."

"All right, have it your way. If you need anything from me just ask any of the deputies to give me a call. I'll make sure they have my phone number at home, too. Let's go, Mac. We've got a lot of work to do in a short period of time. We'll be talking to you later, Freddy."

Shane and McCarthy left the jailhouse and walked to the hotel bar downtown where they got to know each other over a cocktail. By the time they left, Shane had their investigation laid out.

The plan was for Shane to interrogate all the witnesses who made statements to Deputy Sheriff Leone Pickup and The Colonel. He would also handle the investigation of the crime scene. McCarthy would travel to Sing Sing, Auburn Penitentiary and Great Meadow Prison. He would dig through Harry Farnsworth and Freddy Lindsay's inmate files and interview prison personnel who knew them while they had been incarcerated.

They also agreed to meet at the Cattaraugus County Courthouse the following morning, March 21, to talk with The Colonel. Neither of them knew much about Colonel Edward Krieger because they did not normally handle criminal cases.

During their meeting, Shane asked for letters of introduction for McCarthy that would enable him to access Harry Farnsworth and Freddy Lindsay's inmate records at all three prisons. The Colonel assured them that the letters would be ready to pick up that afternoon. Before going any further The Colonel asked if they understood that the grand jury had indicted Freddy Lindsay for First Degree Murder and Felony Murder Committed During the Commission of a Crime for Bernice, but not for her husband, Harold. When Shane asked for a Bill of Particulars that laid out the evidence and the cause for both charges, The Colonel explained he was not compelled to produce the bill because he had an indictment from the grand jury. Shane was doubtful about that statement but said nothing. Clearly, though, The Colonel's response irritated him.

After calling over to the secretarial pool for the case files, The Colonel informed Shane and McCarthy that in addition to the extra murder charge, he had no plans to file against Freddy for the murder of Harold Farnsworth. Shane understood The Colonel was holding murder charges against Freddy for Harry Farnsworth in the wings just in case he was unable to get a conviction for either of the capital murder charges in Bernice's case.

A secretary brought copies of the case files in and The Colonel set up Shane and McCarthy at a desk in an interview room so that they could take their time reading the material. The two defense attorneys scribbled notes on legal pads as they pored over the large pile of documents. Four hours later they left for lunch.

McCarthy wanted to engage in small talk, but Shane would have none of it. They discussed the case as they ate. Shane had a good idea where The Colonel's prosecution was heading, but he would need more information to derail his plans.

When they returned to The Colonel's office, the three letters of introduction were ready for McCarthy. Shane thanked The Colonel for his help and they turned around and left. In the parking lot, Shane told McCarthy to go home and pack for the trip. He wanted him at Auburn Penitentiary on Friday, Great Meadow Prison on Sunday, and Sing Sing on Tuesday. And if all went well, McCarthy would be back late on Wednesday, March 27.

Mac McCarthy headed home and Syd Shane left for the town of Randolph. He wanted to begin interviewing the witnesses who gave statements after the murder. The first name on his list was Florence Adams Searle, wife of Robert Tyler Searle. Florence was a cousin of Bernice. Shane was hoping Florence and her husband had had a lot of contact with Freddy at the Farnsworth farm.

Florence was at home when Shane arrived at the Searle residence, but Robert was out. Shane introduced himself and

Florence graciously invited him in to talk. She led him into the parlor and they sat down next to each other in easy chairs.

"I know you know nothing about the circumstances of your cousin's murder, but I thought you might shed some light on other things," said Shane.

"I would be happy to help you in any way, Mr. Shane, but before I do, I would like to ask you one question. Would that be all right?" she asked.

"Why, certainly it is, Mrs. Searle. Ask away!"

"Are you going to try to get that man Lindsay acquitted of Bernice and Harry's murders?"

"No, ma'am, I assure you that I am not. I am trying to determine if he is guilty of first-degree murder, or of murder while committing a felony. He has already admitted to his crime in writing to the District Attorney, so an acquittal is not likely to occur. I only want what is fair for Alfred Lindsay. No more and no less than that."

"Oh, that is good news. I couldn't have anything to do with setting that wretched man free. Bernice is family, after all."

"Yes. I understand. Now, about those questions, ma'am?"

Shane determined right away that Florence and her husband usually had the Farnsworths come to their house in Randolph whenever they got together. As a result, Florence and Robert had had very little contact with Freddy Lindsay. Shane changed direction and asked about Harry.

"Did you like Bernice's husband, Harry?"

"You know, at first I didn't like him one single bit," Florence confessed. "He was a convicted felon, after all. But when I saw them together over time, it became obvious that they were truly in love with one another. I saw it in the small things they did. They looked at one another often and made eye contact. That was always followed by a small, knowing smile. Other times, it was just the way Bernice would lay her hand on Harry's arm as they sat and talked. Their love was in every laugh they shared together. Their relationship was a very gentle one, I'd say. Bernice was the happiest I had seen her in many, many years...."

Florence teared up and had to stop speaking while she left to get a handkerchief. She dabbed at her tears and continued. "After a while, I grew to like Harry very much. So did my husband, Robert, much to his surprise. Robert respected Harry for being such a hard worker. Bernice would brag to Robert about how handy Harry was around the farm."

"Thank you, Mrs. Searle, I'm sorry to have upset you. Now, this next question may offend you, ma'am, but I need to know the answer to this question if you can provide it. Did Harry cheat on Bernice with another woman?"

"Good Lord, no! They were dedicated to one another. Harry would never have done that!"

Shane moved on, and just as the interview was winding up, the front door to the Searle home flew open. A young boy, fourteen years old, entered the room.

"Hi, ma!" said Theodore Adams Searle. "I'm hungry. What have we got to eat?"

"Teddy Searle! Have you forgotten all of the manners you've been taught, young man? Say hello to Mr. Shane. He's here to talk about that hired man, Lindsay."

"Sorry. Hello, Mr. Shane," Teddy said. "I met that guy."

"You did, son?" said Shane. "Mrs. Searle, would you mind if I talked to your son about Alfred Lindsay?"

"No, as long as you don't go into any details of the unfortunate incident at Bernice's farm, I don't mind."

"Absolutely. I understand completely. So, let's have it, Teddy. How do you know Alfred Lindsay?"

"Well, in the first place I only met him as Freddy Lindsay, not Alfred. In the second place, I met him out at Cousin Bernice's place when I went up there with her and Harry in their car last month. My cousin Bobby Blessing was there when we pulled up to Aunt Bernice's place. He was visiting with his mother and father. Me and Bobby got bored, so we headed out for the woods. We heard some chopping sounds and figured Harry was out there. So we walked through the woods until we found him and Freddy in a little clearing they had created from trees they chopped down. Lindsay was wearing this funny looking cap with a tassel hanging from it. Me and Bobby got a good laugh at that. We thought maybe the guy was an Egyptian or something.

"They took a break while we were there and Freddy asked us if we wanted any squirrels to play with. Of course we said, 'Sure we do!' So he pulls out a neat little red collar with a leash from his pocket. Then he heads out for the woods and disappears. When he got back, he had a gray squirrel in his hands. It was as calm as could be. Freddy slipped the collar over the squirrel's neck and led him around like a dog on a leash! That squirrel was tame as could be. I asked him if I could try my hand at walking the squirrel and Freddy handed it to me. No sooner did he let it go that it started to bite my hands up real bad. I had to drop the squirrel and it ran off into the woods. Somehow it got out of the collar and left it behind on the ground. Bobby picked up the collar and pretty soon the men went back to work on the wood. We left after a while because we were bored watching them chop wood. I know Bobby still has the collar because Freddy never asked him to give it back.

"I saw Freddy one other time in Randolph the next week and he was walking around with a little Chickadee on his shoulder. Everybody in town was amazed to see it! He would brush the bird off of his shoulder and it would fly right back. Sometimes he would put out his hand and the bird would fly over to it and sit right there, calm as could be!

"You know, my dad always tells me that animals are good judges of people. But seeing what that guy did, I don't know if that is really true now."

Shane thanked Teddy for the information. His mother dismissed the boy and told him to go find a snack in the kitchen. Shane then thanked Florence Searle for allowing him to take up her time, said goodbye and left the house. When he reached his car he did not start it up right away. He sat there for a few minutes deep in thought. The story that Teddy had just relayed about Freddy Lindsay disturbed him. Freddy was becoming an enigma. What was he—a vicious double-murderer or a saint who tamed animals?

After a few minutes Shane started the car and headed for Coldspring by way of Coldspring Road. He stopped in to visit Ruell Wheeler, Ira Bennett and William Whitmore. He left each of them knowing little more than what he had gleaned from the reports produced by Leone Pickup on March 8.

Before continuing on to see Fred Houlihan at his garage in Steamburg, Shane made a detour and stopped at the Farnsworth farmhouse to look at the crime scene. He was surprised to find the front door to the house unlocked. He became angry when he entered and found that the home had been emptied. He fully expected to find the crime scene intact. Shane slammed the front door shut behind him and continued on his way to Steamburg.

When he arrived in Steamburg, he asked Fred Houlihan for permission to use the garage phone. Shane called Sheriff Lester Carlson at his office in Little Valley. He reached the sheriff through a switchboard operator.

"Hello, Sheriff Carlson speaking."

"Hello, Sheriff Carlson, this is Syd Shane, defense counsel for Alfred Lindsay. I just came from the Farnsworth farm. The house has been completely emptied! Were you aware of that?"

"Well, now, I can't say that I was, Mr. Shane," Carlson replied. "But I don't know why you are upset. Our investigation of the crime scene was very thorough. I assure you there was no way we missed anything there."

"That's not the point, sheriff, and you know it. My client has been robbed of the right to have a second party analyze that crime scene! I want to know who is responsible for this," Shane said loudly.

Arguing the point with the sheriff proved fruitless as Sheriff Carlson refused to admit anything. Shane was fuming when he hung up the phone. But he gathered his thoughts, calmed down, and interviewed Fred Houlihan. When that was done he decided to call it a day and left for Salamanca and a late dinner with his wife, Zeita Marie Shane. He was lost in thought all the way home. By the time he parked his car in front of his house at 18 Penn Street, he was all worked up again about the crime scene being dismantled before he'd had an opportunity to investigate it.

Dinner did not go well. Shane was distant and for the most part ignored his wife's attempts to make conversation. He was barely aware that his wife brought out their month-old son, J. Michael Shane, to see him after dinner. He murmured something unintelligible and continued ruminating about the crime scene in the Farnsworth farmhouse. His wife finally gave up on him and left him to his own devices for the rest of the evening.

The alarm clock in their bedroom went off at six o'clock on Friday morning, March 23. Shane went out onto the porch and picked up the morning edition of the *Olean Times–Herald* that lay near the front door. His wife went into the kitchen and prepared a pot of coffee. Shane sat down in his easy chair in the living room and looked at the front page of the newspaper. An article about Freddy Lindsay caught his attention and he was surprised to read about the new security measures installed at the county courthouse. The article also mentioned that snipers from the Olean National Guard were posted on the roof of the county jailhouse waiting for Bob Lindsay to arrive with his gang of thieves. Shane was outraged. It was the straw that broke the camel's back.

Shane gulped down his coffee, then showered and dressed

quickly. He breezed by his wife and was out the door by seven o'clock. He headed for downtown Salamanca and bought a copy of the *Salamanca Republican-Press*. The paper stated the security measures at the courthouse may or may not be true, but it still outlined the rumor for everyone to read and decide for himself.

He headed for Randolph, where he bought a copy of the *Randolph Register*. The register was a weekly publication, so the article covered all of the news concerning Freddy from the previous week. It was by far the most damning article of all. It read in part:

April 1 is Early Date Supreme Court Sets for Trial of Lindsey

Taking No Chances

Sheriff Carlson is taking no chances with this man Lindsey. His cell is located on the third floor of the jail and a watch is set at the cell door night and day; the defendant is never out of the sight of some officer..... He is not allowed metal tableware while he eats, for yesterday he complained that the wooden spoon was too large for his mouth and he was given a pressed paper spoon, a quantity of which was obtained from an ice cream saloon. The food he receives is the same as that served to other prisoners but it is prepared for eating before it is handed into the cell....

The police in New York City believe that Lindsey's brother was the mastermind in a recent robbery of a New York theater three weeks ago, where something over $10,000 was taken. The brother is sought, but the Cattaraugus County officials were warned lest the brother organize a gang and attempt a liberation of the man held for murder.....

Armed Guards at Night

Besides two guards who day and night watch
at the Lindsey cell, the regular force at
the county jail is reinforced by two
sharpshooters from the Olean State Guards.
These men are armed with modern guns,
capable of sweeping a path through any mob
which might approach, and the men really
know how to handle their weapons…..

Now Syd Shane was really angry. He knew the entire jury pool in Cattaraugus County had been poisoned by sensational and inaccurate newspaper articles. He headed over to his office in Salamanca and stormed into his office, startling his secretary, Margaret Locklin.

"Get me Sheriff Carlson on the line! I want to speak with him right now!" he commanded.

"Right away, boss!" Margaret responded.

When Margaret had the sheriff on the line, she sat and listened to Shane as he reamed out the sheriff for leaking information concerning his client and the case in general. He accused the sheriff of grandstanding with the placement of Olean National Guard sharpshooters on the roof of the jail. Sheriff Carlson denied most of Shane's accusations and tried to slough off the whole thing on "greedy newspaper men interested only in selling newspapers."

Shane slammed the phone down, cutting off the words of the sheriff, and shot out of the office and got into his car. He arrived at the county courthouse and parked. He walked briskly to the jail that stood behind the courthouse and circled the building looking for signs of the sharpshooters, but saw none. He went into the sheriff's office, which was attached to the jail, and demanded access to the roof of the jail. Sheriff Carlson refused, saying only that it would pose a security risk to allow him on the roof. Shane was so heated that Deputy Sheriff Leone Pickup stood behind the closed office door in case things got out of hand. Shane almost knocked him over as he burst out of Sheriff Carlson's office and left the building.

Looking for a phone, Shane made his way into downtown Little Valley and called his secretary. "Has Mac McCarthy called in yet?" he demanded.

"No, Syd, he hasn't. Do you want me to give him a message when he does?" she asked tentatively.

"Yes. Tell him that he is to come back to Salamanca at once. Tell him to forget about going to the other two prisons. We have to put together a motion for a change of venue and for a Bill of Particulars as soon as possible. Tell him that I will fill him in when he gets back home."

"Yes, sir! I'll tell him all of that when I speak with him. What's going on here, Syd? I've never seen you so angry!"

"I'll fill you in when I get back to the office. I'm at a public telephone and I don't want anyone to overhear me. I have to make a stop at the Salamanca Public Library before I return to the office. I'll see you in couple of hours."

Syd Shane drove to the Salamanca Public Library on Wildwood Street. He sat in the periodical section and pored over the library's collection of local newspapers from March 9 forward. He noted every article he read on a notepad. When he was done, he grabbed lunch on Main Street and then headed for his office.

Margaret informed him when he returned that Mac had called collect from a station just as he was getting ready to board a train that would get him close to Great Meadow Prison. She also said that Mac had called in again after exchanging his ticket, and would be returning to Salamanca that evening.

Shane gave Margaret his list of newspaper articles from the Salamanca Library and told her to go down to the local library, look up the original articles, write down each article verbatim, then return and type her handwritten notes. She grabbed her purse and a notepad and left immediately.

Then Shane went to work on the change of venue. He worked until 5:15 that evening, then went home for dinner, as he was accustomed to doing. He arrived back at this office at seven that evening and continued to work on the motion. Margaret worked on the transcription of the newspaper articles until half past eight. Mac called from his house in Salamanca a few minutes after nine o'clock. Shane filled him in on what he had discovered in the newspapers and they agreed to meet at the office the next morning to continue to work on the change of venue motion and the Bill of Particulars. Shane insisted that Freddy Lindsay's trial be moved out of Cattaraugus County. Shane left for home at 11:15 that evening.

McCarthy arrived at Shane's office the next morning, Saturday, March 23, and the two men brainstormed for a couple of hours. They decided the best way to prove the jury pool had been contaminated by false and misleading articles from area newspapers was to get out and talk to the man on the street. Using a map of the county, they divided the area into four quadrants and selected towns located in each quadrant. McCarthy and Shane each left the office with their list of towns to visit.

They spent all of Saturday, Sunday, and Monday—March 23 through 25—gathering signed affidavits from strangers they approached on the streets of Cattaraugus County. They gathered one hundred signed affidavits in which the deponents of the statements affirmed that they believed Freddy Lindsay could not receive a fair trial in Little Valley. Shane and McCarthy raced to the County Clerk's office in the courthouse. Guy Fargo received the change of venue motion and a motion for a Bill of Particulars and processed it. The paperwork was sent to the Supreme Court in Buffalo by courier.

All one hundred affidavits, as well as a typed copy of the text from every article published in every Cattaraugus County newspaper and the *Buffalo Courier-Expfress* in Buffalo were included in the change of venue motion.

Shane and McCarthy appeared before Clinton T. Horton, Justice of the Supreme Court in Buffalo, on the morning of Wednesday, March 27. Colonel Krieger was also present to answer for the State of New York. Justice Horton asked Syd Shane if he knew how many people refused to sign the affidavit stating that they felt Lindsay could not receive a fair trial. Shane, being an honest man, answered truthfully that it was about the same amount as those who thought that he could not receive a fair trial.

The justice questioned The Colonel, who did not dispute the content of the newspaper articles or the release of Freddy's statement to the press. After he heard brief arguments from The Colonel and Shane, Justice Horton recessed the hearing. He assured both parties that he would render his decision before the commencement of Freddy Lindsay's trial on April 1. There was little to do but wait for the justice's decision.

Thursday, March 28 passed without any news from Buffalo. The business day was almost over on Friday, March 29, when Shane's secretary received a call from the clerk at the Supreme Court in Buffalo. Justice Horton had denied the motion for the change of venue and the motion for a Bill of Particulars. He stated that he agreed with Colonel Krieger that the issuance of the grand jury indictment ruled out the need for a Bill of Particulars.

The basis for his decision to deny the motion for change of venue lay solely on the testimony that Shane gave concerning those who had refused to sign the affidavit. He ruled that if half of the people in the county felt that Lindsay could get a fair trial, then there were indeed plenty of unbiased jurors available to hear the trial. Shane's heart sank. He suspected that the judge had ruled in the state's favor because of his professional experience with Bernice Kenyon Farnsworth. Shane resigned himself to preparing himself the best he could for his client.

When The Colonel got the news of the denial, he crowed like a rooster in a hen house. He relished the small victory he had snatched from Syd Shane and Mac McCarthy. He saw it as a precursor to the victory he would achieve at the conclusion of Freddy Lindsay's trial for murder.

Shane called McCarthy and told him that the trial was still on for Monday. They were prepared to burn the midnight oil Friday night, work all day Saturday and all day Sunday in order to get ready for jury selection. They would also need to spend time with Freddy Lindsay to explain trial proceedings with him.

By Sunday night, Shane was beginning to feel the pull of Old Sparky himself and the thought of Freddy frying in the electric chair sickened him. He knew they had no other options. The die had been cast.

Harry Farnsworth, Crime Scene photo by Walter Wilhelm

**Bernice Kenyon Farnsworth in cellar, Crime Scene photo
by Sylvester Nodler (note axe to the left of body)**

Alfred "Freddy" Lindsay

G. Sydney Shane, Defense Attorney
Photo courtesy of J. Michael Shane

Orla Black

Dr. Marshall L. Hillsman

Deputy Sheriff Leone Pickup pointing to milk cans

Fred Houlihan Garage and Burr's Store

**Bernice Farnsworth's 1930 Chevy Sport Coupe
parked by the Old Cattaraugus County Jail**

**Queensboro Milk Plant, Steamburg, New York early 1940s
Photo courtesy of Mrs. Paul Arrance, Steamburg, NY**

Alfred Lindsay, who
had been in prison
with the slain man

Freddy Lindsay in court

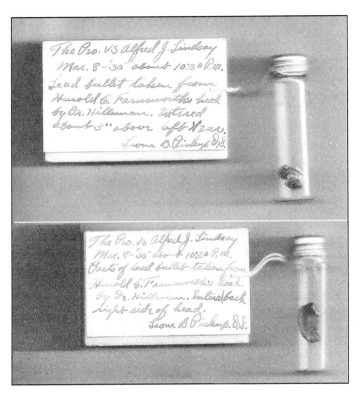

**Two bullets taken from Harry Farnsworth's head
during autopsy by Dr. Marshall Hillsman**

The Axe

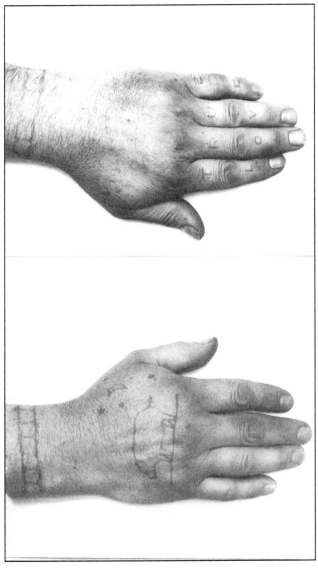

Freddy Lindsay's hands

William W. Whitmore and Ira Newton Bennett

Florence, Robert and Teddy Searle
Florence was a cousin of Bernice Kenyon Farnsworth

Amos O. Squire M. D.

to be Nominated by the

ROTARY CLUB OF OSSINING, N. Y.

for Director   .

ROTARY INTERNATIONAL

☙ 1935 - 1936 ☙

Doctor Amos O. Squire
Photo courtesy of Ossining Historical Society

Warden Lewis E. Lawes and Principal Keeper John J. Sheehy
at Sing Sing Correctional Facility
Photo courtesy of Ossining Historical Society

Door from the inner cells to the "Last Mile" at Sing Sing
Photo courtesy of Ossining Historical Society

Old Sparky witness pews at Sing Sing
Photo courtesy of Ossining Historical Society

"Old Sparky" at Sing Sing Correctional Facility
Photo courtesy of Ossining Historical Society

CHAPTER TEN

THE ROADS THAT LED INTO LITTLE VALLEY WERE ALL JAMMED with cars and horse drawn buggies by eight o'clock on Monday morning, April 1, 1935. Every available parking spot on every street within blocks of the courthouse was taken. The county tow truck operator could not keep up with the calls from town residents whose driveways were blocked by spectator's cars. Some of the narrower streets in town were not passable, as cars and buggies lined both sides. Horse manure littered the streets and the constant flow of traffic mashed it into the asphalt on Court Street. Sheriff's deputies directed the traffic and stood guard around the courthouse and the jail.

Little Valley had not seen crowds of this size gather for a trial since Cynthia Buffum's case in 1914. Every day, before a packed courtroom, Mrs. Buffum was tried, convicted and sentenced to die in the Auburn electric chair for poisoning her husband, Willis Buffum, with horse liniment. The situation was repeated when she was granted a new trial on appeal. But Mrs. Buffum lost her nerve when the jury began deliberations on the charge of first-degree murder at the close of the second trial. She pleaded guilty to second-degree murder three minutes before the court convened to hear the jury's verdict.

On this Monday, enterprising street vendors set up shop on Court Street to peddle food and drink from makeshift carts parked on the sidewalk in front of courthouse. Newspaper boys walked through the crowd on the courthouse lawn. They created an oddly syncopated chorus as they hawked the morning newspapers from the *Salamanca Republican-Press,* the *Olean Times-Herald,*

Randolph Register, Jamestown Post and the *Buffalo Courier-Express.*

Sheriff Carlson watched the scene unfold from a large second-story courthouse window. The size of the crowd made him uneasy. He wished the off-duty National Guard sharpshooters whom he had hired after Freddy arrived at the jail were still positioned on the roof. If it weren't for Syd Shane, he would have posted them again in a flash. The Colonel had forced him to remove them after Shane's protest last week. And no one wanted to give Shane any more ammunition for an appeal, if one was made. Carlson had recently been forced to admit to several newspaper reporters that he had hired the sharpshooters. He still felt stung by the backlash of those articles. Most readers felt as though he had lied about the sharpshooters through omission. Sheriff Carlson wanted this trial to be over in the worst way.

By 8:45 a.m., Court Street was jammed with pedestrians all the way from Sixth to Ninth streets. The atmosphere was circus-like as the roving vendors returned and walked through the crowd peddling their wares. The people closest to the courthouse doors began jockeying for a good position, hoping to be one of the lucky few allowed to enter the courtroom. Deputies Nix and Arrowsmith guarded the locked courthouse doors and kept the crowd at a safe distance.

By 8:55 a.m., the crowd was buzzing with mild annoyance as a phalanx of deputies cleared a passageway for a single line of men who followed closely behind them. The line was made up of reporters from every newspaper in the area. Lynn Blessing walked at the tail end of the line. He was the sole representative from the Blessing-Kenyon family.

When the line of men reached the courthouse entrance, one deputy unlocked the door while the other stood guard in case the crowd tried to charge the open door. The men entered the building without incident. The mood of the crowd was different from the crowd that had gathered for Freddy's arraignment on March 20. This crowd was made up of lookie-loos and thrill-seekers. Despite Sheriff Carlson's worries, there was nothing angry or ugly about them. The people just wanted to be near history in the making.

Lynn Blessing and the reporters entered the courtroom and sat in the front row of the audience section. The Colonel and Mac McCarthy were already arguing about the accuracy of the Evidence List. They continued wrangling with legal issues for almost another hour before the court was finally ready to convene for jury selection. The bailiff went out to the hallway and took a roll call of the potential jurors milling about. Out of a list of one hundred men, only eighty-nine were present. The bailiff went back into the courtroom and presented Judge George Larkin with the list of men.

When deputies Nix and Arrowsmith received word that jury selection was about to begin, they opened the doors and began counting off spectators as they entered the courtroom. They stopped the line when they had reached the capacity of the audience section. A deputy then roped off the foot of the stairway and stood guard, refusing to allow any more people upstairs. At that point, the front doors to the courthouse were flung open and people poured into the lobby until it was full to capacity.

Upstairs in the courtroom, Colonel Krieger sat at the table for the prosecution, located to the left of the judge's bench. Shane sat with McCarthy at the defense table to the right of the bench. Undersheriff Charles Wing and Deputy Donald McDonald sat at the end of the defense table on either side of Freddy Lindsay.

At 10:20 a.m., when all the spectators were seated, Judge Larkin opened the trial and jury selection commenced. Syd Shane's argument for the change of venue seemed vindicated as he and The Colonel began examining the potential jurors. The Colonel and Shane had developed a list of questions for the potential jurors:

Have you read or talked about this case?

Have you formed an opinion regarding the guilt or innocence of the defendant by reading or talking about the case?

Have you talked with anyone who presumed to know the facts of the case?

If you find upon evidence submitted that the defendant is guilty, will you so vote, unmindful of the consequences of such a vote?

Do you believe in capital punishment?

What newspaper articles have you read about the case?

Do you know the district attorney or any member of the Sheriff's Department and particularly Elmer Miller or Leone Pickup?

Do you know Fred Houlihan of Steamburg, Ira Bennett of Randolph, or Nora Moynihan of Randolph?

Do you know Lieutenant George of the State Police?

The first to take the stand was John P. Hackett of Randolph. He was excused for bias when it was discovered he was a neighbor of the Farnsworths and that his brother had taken up residence at their farmhouse.

Hackett was followed by Percy Paisley of Randolph. Paisley was excused when he said, "I don't believe in capital punishment."

Paisley was followed by Anthony Rojek of Salamanca. Rojek was disqualified when The Colonel asked him, "Can you tell me, Mr. Rojek, if you have formed an opinion on this case?"

"I think I got my opinion all set," Rojek replied.

"So you could give me your verdict in this case right now?"

"Yes, I could!" a grinning Rojek answered emphatically, causing a burst of laughter to erupt from the audience.

Judge Larkin told the bailiff to go over and tell the audience that their presence in the courtroom was not mandatory and they would be removed if they could not be quiet.

Rojek was disqualified by the judge and he was followed by Melvin Wilcox of Great Valley. Wilcox was disqualified after he was questioned by The Colonel about his belief in capital punishment.

"I don't believe in capital punishment. I can't judge a man to be killed!" Wilcox said.

Judge Larkin was becoming concerned about the trend developing in front of him. Thankfully, the first juror was selected when court reconvened following a short recess for lunch. The juror's name was William Wixon, an oil worker from the town of Limestone. Wixon was accepted by the State when he was asked if he believed in capital punishment.

"I believe firmly in capital punishment," Wixon stated.

The unsettling pattern of juror rejection resumed as eleven more potential jurors were excused by the judge, the State and the defense. David Wing, a milk tester from Hinsdale, became juror number 2. He was followed soon by juror number 3, Eber Russell, an electrician from the town of Cattaraugus.

The prospective jurors continued to come and go in a steady stream at the witness box. Judge Larkin, alarmed at the rate of juror attrition, called for County Clerk, Guy Fargo, to draw up another list of fifty prospective jurors. The clerk drew paper slips of names of eligible men from a wooden box. He did this quietly at the front of the courtroom while the questioning of prospective jurors continued.

Sixteen more men left the courtroom without being selected and everyone was showing signs of wear. Judge Larkin called for a short recess to give them all a break.

Court reconvened at 3:15 p.m., and the interlude seemed to have been just what the doctor ordered. Juror number 4, Arthur White, was selected within ten minutes. White was a retired salesman from Olean.

Jury selection ground on for two more hours, during which four more jurors were selected. Juror number 5 was Patrick Hogan, a farmer from Carrollton. Juror number 6 was William Ehbauer, a sheet metal worker from Olean. Juror number 7 was Frank Bassinger, a farmer from Dayton. Juror number 8 was Elmer Walker, a farmer from Carrollton.

By then it was 5:30 p.m., and Judge Larkin announced that he was ready to adjourn for the day. He got an assurance from Guy Fargo that he and the Sheriff's Department would have the additional prospective jurors available for the selection process the next morning when court reconvened. He advised all of those involved in the case to report back to the court the next morning at nine o'clock. He told the eight jurors who were seated in the jury box that they, too, should report in at the same time. He pounded his gavel on the bench and left the courtroom. The first day of Freddy's trial for murder came to an anti-climactic end.

But the audience refused to leave the courtroom until Freddy Lindsay was ushered out by deputies Wing and McDonald. The room buzzed with excitement as the audience members discussed the proceeding they had just witnessed. Each planned on being very popular when they got home. The county folk were thirsty for news of the trial. The story behind the murders and the identity of the woman that Freddy murdered had galvanized their interest.

Syd Shane and Mac McCarthy packed their paperwork into their valises and walked out of the courtroom together. They ignored The Colonel completely. They maneuvered their way through the crowd in front of the courthouse and made their way across Court Street to the parking lot. When they reached their cars they realized that there was no way they could drive anywhere, due to the gridlock that paralyzed the entire town. So, they sat in McCarthy's car and discussed their first day in court.

"What do you think of Krieger as a prosecutor?" asked McCarthy.

"I'm impressed and then I'm not," said Shane. "He seems a very efficient fellow, but I think he's lacking something very important. I don't think he's a great litigator. He doesn't seem confident standing in front of the court. It's just a feeling I have. We'll see how he performs after we select the jury."

"Do you think that will give us an edge with the jury?" asked McCarthy.

"Without sounding like our esteemed client, Mr. Freddy Lindsay, I don't think there is much that will make any difference in this case," Shane said. "Did you notice the type of men on the jury? We're going up against common, solid, hardworking Christians. In their book, you don't kill a woman and you don't take an axe to her, either. None of those men are going to have any problem with sending Freddy to his death. Somehow we must convince them that Freddy does not deserve to die! We have a steep, uphill battle waiting for us."

"The case is starting to get to you, isn't it, Syd."

"Yes, it's starting to get to me. That man's life is in our hands and I am convinced he does not deserve to die! Damn it! He simply does not meet the criteria for First Degree Murder or Murder During the Commission of a Felony."

Shane and McCarthy gave up waiting for traffic to thin out and decided to stroll through downtown Little Valley. The shops that were open were doing a thriving business. They got lucky and found an empty table at the hotel restaurant and had dinner. When they were done, they walked back to their cars and made their way back to Salamanca through congested traffic.

Shane drove directly to his office and arrived there at half passed seven. He called his wife, Zeita, to let her know he was at the office, then spent the next several hours lost in thought, sitting in a haze of cigarette smoke. Every once in a while he got up and pulled a law book off of a shelf and researched one case or another. He paced back and forth on the carpeted floor. Exhausted, he left for home at 9:30. Zeita tried to engage him in a conversation about the trial but he avoided it. They went to bed at ten o'clock.

Five hours later, at three o'clock in the morning, Zeita woke to find Shane sitting at the kitchen table in front of an ashtray overflowing with cigarette butts. She leaned against the kitchen doorway and stared at him. Shane was so lost in thought that he was unaware of her presence. She shrugged her shoulders and went back to bed.

At the same hour, Freddy lay on the bed in his cell with his hands behind his head. He stared at the blank ceiling above him. The hate and revulsion that emanated from the audience section crowd had bored its way into his back as he sat in the courtroom earlier in the day. He was worried about having to sit in the courtroom every day for as many days as the trial might last.

Sleep would not come as he lay there. He closed his eyes for a minute and all he could see was Old Sparky. The vision was spectral and it frightened Freddy so thoroughly that his heart raced and he hyperventilated. He sat up and struggled to control his breathing and the panic running amuck within him.

"Hey!" said the deputy at the cell door. "Are you okay in there?"

"Yeah, I'm fine. I'm just thirsty. Get me a drink of water, would ya?" said Freddy.

"Doesn't that son of a bitch ever sleep?" the deputy asked his partner, who was also stationed at the cell door.

"No. And I doubt you would sleep either if you were up for First Degree Murder!"

The deputy returned with a paper cup filled with water and passed it to Freddy. Freddy drank the water, handed the paper cup back to the deputy and lay back down on the bed with his hands behind his head. He returned to worrying about sitting in the courtroom the next day.

The situation was different with The Colonel. He had waited around in his office until the traffic outside had thinned, and then drove home to Salamanca. He ate a late dinner of roast beef with mashed potatoes and gravy with his family and they had a lively discussion about the events at the trial in Little Valley. He went to bed at half past ten and fell asleep right away.

Lynn Blessing had waited out the traffic, too, and got home at 7:30 that night. His wife, Edith, was disappointed that the trial had not started yet. She was anxious to put the matter of her sister's death behind them. Already the Kenyon sisters spoke less and less about Bernice. They did not want to be reminded of the pain attached to their loss, or of the shame that the circumstances of her death had brought to their doorstep. Bernice had become the woman in the family about whom no one wanted to speak. Her fall from grace was complete.

CHAPTER ELEVEN

TUESDAY, APRIL 2, 1935 BEGAN JUST LIKE THE DAY BEFORE. THE crowd that gathered early in the morning had grown to an enormous size by 8:45. Street vendors were already in place as they anticipated another lucrative day at the courthouse. Many of the stores in the downtown area of Little Valley opened early to accommodate the crowd congregating on Main Street and to capitalize on its needs.

The entire roster of deputies from the sheriff's department was on duty around the courthouse, the jail, and on the streets of Little Valley. Sheriff Carlson thought about temporarily deputizing retired deputies, as the task of controlling the town was growing far too great a task for his small force to handle. He prayed that the throng would be as calm and well behaved as they had been on Monday.

At 8:50 a.m., Lynn Blessing and the group of reporters were escorted through the crowd and admitted through the courthouse doors. When word came down that all were seated in the courtroom, the deputies at the door once again counted out each spectator as they were admitted entrance to the courtroom. Once the spectator section was filled, the doors to the courthouse lobby were thrown open to the public so they could assemble in the lobby.

Guy Fargo conducted a roll call of the eight selected jurors and then went out to the hallway and conducted a roll call of the prospective jurors in the crowded hallway. He also verified that a small group of subpoenaed witnesses were present, in case the trial was able to begin that day. Fargo went into the courtroom and placed the roll sheets on the bench for Judge Larkin to review when he entered and took the bench.

Freddy Lindsay stared at the courtroom floor as he was escorted in by two deputies. He was led to the defense table where Syd Shane and Mac McCarthy were already sitting. The two deputies sat Freddy down then took seats on opposite sides of him. The courtroom buzzed with chatter until Judge Larkin entered from the rear of the courtroom and re-opened the court at 9:15 a.m. The process of jury selection began where it left off the previous afternoon.

Four more jurors were questioned and excused or disqualified before juror number 9, John Metzler, a farmer from Ellicottville, was selected. The next juror, Leon H. Miller, was excused because he was a client of The Colonel's law firm, Krieger and Prey, in Salamanca.

Miller was followed by Lionel Hitchcock of Humphrey, who was excused after he said he had already formed an opinion on the case and could not return a verdict of first-degree murder. Several more prospective jurors were questioned and disqualified before juror number 10, Lewis Vance, a machine operator from Coldspring, was selected.

More prospective jurors came and went from the witness stand but finally, Bradley Stone, a farmer from East Otto, became juror number 11. He was followed by seven more men who were excused for a variety of reasons including deafness, sickness and the need to tend to their farms. The court recessed for lunch at half past twelve. Many spectators in the audience section took out food they had brought from home and ate in their seats, rather than take the chance of losing their place if they left for lunch.

The judge reopened the trial at two o'clock. The first prospective juror to be examined was Guy Casler of Randolph. He testified that he had known Harry Farnsworth for four or five months and that he had formed a definite opinion about the case.

He was excused by the judge.

Freddy Lindsay had a long consultation with Shane and McCarthy about the next man, William Rhodes of Conewango. They excused Mr. Rhodes at the conclusion of their consultation. Ralph Schultz of Little Valley, the seventieth man to be questioned, was also excused by the defense.

The next three men to sit in the witness box and be examined were Charles Shaffer of Olean, Mace Phillips of Olean, and Grayden Williams of Ashford. All three were excused after testifying that they had formed an opinion on the case.

It was with great relief to Judge Larkin when Lyle Roblee, a farmer from Freedom, was selected as juror number 12. But before The Colonel or Shane could make a move to begin the trial, Judge Larkin spoke to them about a decision he had made early on in the jury selection process.

"Now that we have determined who will sit on the jury of this trial, I want to talk to the prosecution and the defense. On September first of 1933, Section 358-A of the New York Code of Criminal procedures came into effect. This law provides for the selection of one or two additional jurors to be selected in felony cases. This is done in case one or more of the jurors become incapacitated during a trial. In accordance with that law I have decided that in this case I will instruct both parties to begin the selection of a thirteenth juror. This thirteenth juror will sit with the other twelve jurors and he will hear all the evidence as it is brought before this court. Bear with me as you select one more juror whom we will call an 'alternate juror.' Are there any questions?"

Neither the prosecution nor the defense objected or questioned the historic decision. The bailiff called a few more prospective jurors in from the hallway and jury selection continued in its search for one more juror.

Mills Kamery from Olean, Joe Lewis from Ischua, and

Adam Learn of Ischua were excused. Juror number thirteen was Charles Eberts, a farmer from Mansfield. The jury was completed at three o'clock. In all, seventy-eight men were called to the stand to be examined as prospective jurors.

Judge Larkin gave instructions to the bailiff that the jury would be sequestered in special rooms at the county jail and guarded at all times by sheriff's deputies when they were not in court.

After determining that both parties were ready to proceed, the judge opened the testimony phase of the trial with four words: "All right. People open."

An almost inaudible but excited whisper rose from the audience members, thrilled at their luck in being present for the opening of the Freddy Lindsay murder trial. The Colonel rose from his seat at the counsel table and walked over to the juror's box. He cleared his throat and began to speak.

"May it please the court, gentlemen of the jury: I shall be quite brief in my opening remarks for this case. The grand jury of this county, on the twentieth of March, 1935, returned an indictment charging Alfred J. Lindsay with the crime of murder in the first degree, in that, on the fifth day of March, with deliberation and premeditation, he killed one Bernice G. Farnsworth by striking her with an axe. There is a second count of the indictment to which I will refer a little later.

"We will show you the facts leading up to this homicide. We will show you that Harry Farnsworth, the husband of the woman who is alleged to have been killed by this defendant, met Alfred J. Lindsay at Great Meadow Prison, in this state, from which they were both discharged on the thirteenth day of August 1934. Farnsworth had previously become acquainted with Miss Bernice Kenyon, a highly respected woman of this community, and following his discharge from Great Meadow, met Miss Kenyon and they were married and came to this county to live. They purchased what is known as the McGraw Hill Farm on what is known as McGraw Hill Road, in the town of Coldspring, close to the line of the Town of Randolph."

The Colonel went on to give the physical location of the farmhouse in question and then described how and when the defendant came to reside at the Farnsworth farm. Syd Shane sat listening raptly to The Colonel's opening argument, waiting for him to make a particular statement.

The Colonel continued, "We will show that one of these kindhearted neighbors took the defendant in, fed him, was nice to him, was kind and hospitable. We will show you that he repaid the hospitality by stealing some of her personal effects."

Shane jumped up from the defense table and shouted, "Objection! If Your Honor please, I...."

"Just a minute!" interrupted Judge Larkin.

"If Your Honor please, I...," Shane said again in another attempt to voice his objection.

"I suggest that you not go into that until I have a chance to see whether that statement is competent," the judge said as he turned to the court stenographer. "Strike that out and the jury will disregard that statement."

Colonel Krieger furrowed his eyebrows and continued his opening statement. He talked about how Freddy Lindsay had stayed in the abandoned house belonging to Nora Moynihan's brother. He told the jury that here in the courtroom was one man who could account for the correct time the tragic events occurred at the Farnsworth farmhouse on Tuesday, March 5, 1935. "There is only one man in this courtroom who knows what happened that day. That man is the defendant," The Colonel said as he pointed his finger at Freddy Lindsay.

He told them that Freddy had been arrested in New York City three days after the bodies were discovered by Ira Bennett and William Whitmore. He described the wounds on Bernice

Farnsworth's body and that a bloodstained axe was found nearby.

The Colonel told the jury about the statement Freddy Lindsay had given him and that the story was implausible except for Freddy's admission of guilt. Then The Colonel spoke of the second indictment against Alfred J. Lindsay and explained to the jury that it needed to find he perpetrated a felony while committing the homicide.

The Colonel ended his opening statement, "We will ask the court to further instruct you, under the second count of this indictment, that if you find the defendant committed a felony while committing this homicide, then he is guilty of murder in the first degree. In either count, gentlemen, we shall ask you for that verdict. I do not believe any twelve men can say there could be any result other than that, for which the People will ask you at the close of its case. Thank you."

Shane leaned over and whispered in McCarthy's, "If that was brief, I'd hate to see a long opening from him! Keep your opening short, Mac. The jury looks bored."

Shane rose and addressed the court, "If the court please, we wish to note an exception to the District Attorney's remarks to the jury pointing to the fact that the defendant and Mr. Farnsworth met in the Great Meadow State Prison and ask the Court to instruct this jury to disregard that remark as prejudicial to this defendant."

"I decline to do that. You have the exception," Larkin said.

"Exception, Your Honor," Shane replied, "In view of the District Attorney's opening, Your Honor, I now ask for a dismissal of the second count in the indictment."

"I will deny that."

"Exception."

"Defendant open."

Mac McCarthy lifted his large frame from the chair at the defense table and approached the jury. He cut an impressive figure in his suit, fashioned expressly for him by a tailor in New York City. His diamond cufflinks caught errant rays of light and sparkled now and then as he moved his arms. He looked each of the jurors in the eye, then opened for the defense.

"May it please the Court, gentlemen of the jury: The defendant, Alfred J. Lindsay, is brought here today by the Power of the State to answer a charge of murder in the first degree. Less than a month ago, at a lonely farm on one of the back roads of Cattaraugus County, Bernice Farnsworth was killed. We think the facts will show that it all happened very quickly, so quickly that she probably never even knew or had a chance to think about it. That does not justify it. I would not have it so. But she is dead and all the power of the State and all the investigation we may conduct at this trial cannot call her back to life."

McCarthy asked that the State present their case as a result of their investigation rather than to persecute the defendant. He said he would not spend time discussing the facts of the case in his opening statement because the trial would surely suffice in bringing them forward to the jury. He reminded the jurors that Freddy Lindsay was innocent until the facts of the case proved him guilty of Bernice Farnsworth's murder. Then he warned them to be aware of extraneous matters that would be brought into the trial. He asked that they consider only the facts.

In closing he said, "I can say shortly, gentlemen, what we ask at your hands is a fair and impartial trial for this defendant, which we believe will result in acquittal on the charge contained in the indictment you are trying today. To such a fair trial this defendant is entitled. More than that he does not ask. Less than that he should not have. Thank you."

McCarthy sat down and Shane patted him on the shoulder. Judge Larkin instructed the State to call their first witness.

"The State calls Ira Bennett to the stand, Your Honor," said The Colonel.

The bailiff went to the courthouse door, opened it and called out the name Ira Bennett. Ira appeared and followed the bailiff to the witness stand. He stood, raised his right hand, placed his left hand on a bible and was sworn in. Ira Bennett took the stand.

Through questioning, Ira stated he was a close neighbor to Bernice and that he last saw the Farnsworths alive on Monday, March 4, at his farm. He admitted that he met Freddy Lindsay in December 1934, but had little interaction with him in the following months. The Colonel then asked Ira to describe the events that led up to his discovery of the bodies from the point where he instructed William Whitmore to go and deliver the wood rack to the Farnsworth farm.

Ira's testimony was peppered with objections from Shane. Although Ira had been instructed to tell only what he had done and not what he or anyone else had said, he kept quoting himself and William. When describing Bernice's body in the cellar he said, "Mrs. Farnsworth lay to the left of the stairs. I came back up to the head of the stairs and told Mr. Whitmore to come down there."

Shane shot up and said, "Just a minute, please. I object to any conversation with Mr. Whitmore!"

Ira looked right at Syd Shane and said, "I didn't have any conversation with him. I just asked him to come downstairs!"

The audience laughed loudly at his statement, which infuriated Judge Larkin, who was again growing tired of their outbursts.

"Now, wait a minute!" he said to the bailiff, "Warn those people to be quiet!"

The Colonel continued with his examination of Ira and progressed through the condition of Bernice Farnsworth's body at the time it was found, and then on to the phone call Ira made to Deputy Sheriff Leone Pickup. He asked if Bernice's car was present at the farm. "Would you know Mrs. Farnsworth's car if you saw it?"

"Yes," replied Ira.

The Colonel turned to Sheriff Carlson, who was standing at the courtroom windows, and asked, "Is the car out there now, sheriff?"

The sheriff answered, "Yes."

"Will you step to the window, Mr. Bennett," asked The Colonel, "and see if you recognize the car out there as hers?"

Ira got up from the witness stand, walked to the window and stood next to Carlson. Together they looked out the window and discussed what they saw.

Shane rose and objected, "If Your Honor please, I think I will object to any identification in the presence of the jurors, by this witness, of some object that the jury cannot see."

At the same time, The Colonel warned the sheriff, "No conversation, Mr. Carlson, please."

Shane continued, "And furthermore to the conversation that is being conducted between the sheriff and the witness."

Ira Bennett, who had turned and walked away from the window, decided to go back and take another look at the car.

"Just a minute!" exclaimed Judge Larkin, "Come back here, witness! Send the witness back here."

The audience broke into laughter again.

The judge turned to the bailiff. "Tell those people this is not an amusement place and if they do not conduct themselves properly, I will have the place cleared. This is not a joking matter. Now conduct yourselves accordingly!"

The audience quieted down at the threat of being removed from the courtroom. After The Colonel asked Ira a few more questions, the judge called for a short recess. When court resumed, The Colonel continued his examination.

"Mr. Bennett," he began, "during the recess, did you go down to the yard here and look at the car?"

"Yes, sir," Ira answered.

"And is that car that you looked at, the one that now sits out there in the yard, the same car which you knew as Mrs. Farnsworth's car?"

"Yes, sir."

"Why is that?"

"Two jammed fenders where you sit cans on the back end."

"Milk cans?"

"Yes, sir."

"Mr. Bennett, in reference to those two dead bodies that you described, did you know those people in their lifetimes?"

"Well, not up until a year ago!"

Judge Larkin stared sternly at the audience who did not dare laugh at Ira's remark.

"Well," continued The Colonel, "then you knew them both while they were living?"

"Yes."

"And you knew them as Harold C. Farnsworth and Bernice G. Kenyon Farnsworth?"

"Yes."

"And are they the people whose bodies you found at the Farnsworth home?"

"Yes."

Colonel Krieger turned and addressed Shane. "You may ask."

Shane probed Ira about the date and time of his discovery of the two bodies.

"Did you observe a loaf of bread hanging in some kind of hamper?" he asked.

"No, not that day," Ira replied.

"Did you later make some observations?"

"Yes."

"In regard to the loaf of bread?"

"Yes. It might have been there when we went back the second time."

Shane asked Ira to describe the breadbasket and the manner in which it hung on the door handle of the mudroom in the rear of the Farnsworth house. He moved on to the placement of Bernice and Harold's arms, and how their hands were positioned in the same exact way. Shane asked who took the crime scene photos and at what time they were taken. Shane had no further questions and returned to his seat.

The Colonel, on redirect of Ira Bennett, established that nothing in the Farnsworth's house had been moved up to the time the crime scene pictures were taken. He asked about the snowfall from the previous night, and established that the wind blew hard enough to pile snow on the mudroom floor.

Syd Shane, on recross examination, established that the only snow found in the kitchen was brought in on the shoes of the people who entered the house.

Ira Bennett was excused when The Colonel had no further questions for him.

William Whitmore was called to the stand. Upon examination by The Colonel, William reiterated the testimony that Ira had given concerning the discovery of the bodies on March 8. William proved no better at avoiding conversation between him and Ira at the farmhouse. Shane bopped up and down several times, registering objections to William's testimony.

"Where did you find Mr. Farnsworth's body?" asked The Colonel.

"The same place as Mr. Bennett," he replied.

The audience showed restraint and didn't laugh.

Shane objected to the answer and The Colonel asked William to answer the question again in his own words. The Colonel ended his questioning after determining that William did not see a metal cashbox in the room near where Harry's body lay.

Syd Shane approached William and asked about his stay at the Farnsworth farmhouse shortly after the couple purchased the property. William had difficulty describing the location of the bodies in the house because he was nervous testifying in front of such a large group of people. But Shane was patient and William finally settled down. He asked William if Harry Farnsworth had a bad temper and beat his animals. William denied this, so Shane quoted what William had told him when he visited William at the Bennett farm. He used his notepad for reference.

"You were asked this question, were you not: 'And took pretty good care of his stock.' "

"Yes."

"And you answered, 'He treated them all right, but he was mean on the club, knocked, clubbed and pounded the horses around.' Did you make that answer?"

"No. Just one horse."

"Answer my question! Did you make that answer to that question?"

"Not in that way."

"So, what I say you answered to my question is not the correct answer to the question I asked you? Yes or no?"

"No."

"Did you also say this to me, 'He had one horse that was heavey and didn't want to go. He used to abuse that one.' "

"Yes."

"He pounded him to get him to go?"

"Yes."

"You did make that answer?"

"Yes."

"But you did not make the first part of the answer that I read to you?"

"No, sir."

"Now, you are willing to swear to that, are you, Mr. Whitmore?"

"Yes, sir."

"That is all."

Colonel Krieger stood and said, "That is all, Mr. Whitmore."

William scurried down from the witness stand and left the courtroom visibly upset by the grilling he had received from Shane.

George Middleton, the county coroner, was called next by The Colonel. Through a series of questions and answers, he established who was on the farm when he arrived, where the bodies were found, and the condition of the bodies after a cursory examination. The coroner also testified about the removal of the bodies, which were taken to the county morgue. When he was asked to describe in detail the wounds on both bodies, Shane stood up and objected on the grounds that the coroner was an undertaker by profession and not a licensed physician. The judge sustained the objection and The Colonel had to abandon that line of questioning. Middleton was furious. His face turned red and his lips were pursed so tightly they turned white.

The Colonel then questioned Middleton about the presence of gunpowder burns above Harry Farnsworth's right eye. When Shane raised objections stating Middleton was not an expert on powder burns, The Colonel ended his examination of the coroner.

Coroner Middleton became hostile during cross-examination when Shane, trying to establish Middleton's credibility, pressed him to name recent gunshot victims upon whom he had found powder burns. He provided the name of a man he received as a gunshot victim just prior to picking up the Farnsworth bodies at the farmhouse.

"Well, now, what other occasion?" asked Shane.

"I refuse to quote names, because I can't remember them," Middleton shot back.

"You don't care to answer the question?"

"I don't care to answer the question."

"That is all."

The Colonel stood and excused the coroner and called Clifford C. Cheney to the stand. The coroner shot an angry look at Shane and McCarthy as he stormed by them on his way out of the courtroom. Shane could not have cared less about Middleton's reaction. His client was the only person he cared about when he entered a courtroom. In Shane's opinion, you didn't get the truth out of people by handling them with kid gloves.

Clifford Cheney was a civil engineer presently serving as Superintendent of Public Works for the City of Salamanca. He had been hired by The Colonel to render a blueprint of all three levels of the Farnsworth farmhouse. The Colonel set up the blueprint on an easel that faced the jury. Cheney testified that the blueprint had been produced after he'd made a careful series of measurements at the farmhouse. He identified the location of the bodies with rectangles drawn using dotted lines. He gave testimony as to the exact position of the bodies in relation to stairways and nearby walls.

The audience gasped when Cheney described the blood that had dripped down to the cellar from the floor above, forming a pool of blood-soaked dirt surrounding Bernice. The remainder of Cheney's testimony concerned measurements of the distances to Steamburg from the farm and to the spot where the milk cans were found.

On cross-examination, Shane was able to get Cheney to admit he was a little confused about the location of things in the blueprint. Then he established that many things were missing from the blueprint, things like the woodpile, the table the incubator lay on, and a woodbin located in the southeast corner of the cellar. The remainder of Cheney's testimony centered on other items omitted from the blueprint and the failing light of day. There were two redirect and three recross examinations before Cheney was excused.

The last witness called on Tuesday, April 2, 1935, was

Sylvester Nodler, the photographer who had taken the crime scene photos. Nodler testified he had taken only one photo of Bernice Farnsworth's body in the cellar because the light was very poor down there. He said he could not use his electric lighting equipment because there was no electricity in the farmhouse.

He identified each of the other photos The Colonel produced and described when he took it and his position as he took the photo. As they proceeded identifying each photo, The Colonel asked the court to enter and mark it as evidence. The court received the photographs and The Colonel showed them to the jury. The jurors paid particular attention to the photo of Bernice lying in the cellar. The Colonel turned Nodler over to the defense.

Using Clifford Cheney's blueprint, Syd Shane walked Nodler through his positions in the house at the time he took each photo. Several times he asked Nodler to explain why he had not taken a different photo or used a different angle. Nodler's answers were short and accurate. The last question he was asked concerned the length of the time exposure for Bernice's photo. Nodler admitted that the exposure of the photo was under-timed.

At 5:15 p.m., Judge Larkin announced that court would adjourn for the day and he instructed everyone to return at ten o'clock the next morning.

The jurors filed out of the jury box and were escorted out by sheriff's deputies through the exit at the back of the courtroom. They descended the stairway to the first floor. The deputies continued to lead the group of twelve men to the sheriff's office and then into special rooms in the jail designed specifically for sequestered juries. The jurors were assigned two men to a room. All of their meals were brought in and they were told they were not allowed any contact with the outside world. As a result, no phones, newspapers, magazines or radios were available to them.

The courtroom spectators waited patiently for the sheriff's deputies at the defense table to handcuff Freddy and shuffle him out of the courtroom. The events of the first afternoon of the trial caused them to talk excitedly with one another, their voices filling the courtroom, the hallway and the stairway down to the lobby.

The crowd in the lobby swooped down on the exiting spectators like hungry vultures. The air in the courthouse and the lawn in front of it was electric. The news of that day's trial flowed through the crowd and energized it.

Deputy Sheriff Leone Pickup was surprised when several families that had traveled to Little Valley from distant towns attempted to pitch tents on the courthouse lawn. They clearly intended to camp on the lawn for the duration of the trial. When Pickup forced them to pack up, they moved to squatter camps temporarily established on vacant property outside of town.

Colonel Krieger was not enjoying the smugness that he had felt at the close of the previous day. Syd Shane had beaten him up a little during today's proceedings and that didn't sit well with him. He went down to the first floor and locked himself in his office, spending the time poring over the mountain of paperwork related to the case. He was looking for a way to turn the tables on Shane and McCarthy. The Colonel remained in his office until seven o'clock and made his way home through extremely heavy traffic. He ate a late dinner with his family, but he did not display the cockiness of the previous evening. He had underestimated Shane and McCarthy and had paid a price.

In the meantime, Syd Shane and Mac McCarthy headed over to the hotel restaurant and waited for a dinner table. They ordered dinner and once again McCarthy tried to make light conversation.

"Aren't you ever off duty, Syd?" Mac asked jokingly.

"No, and you shouldn't be either. You're a very good lawyer, Mac, but you will never achieve greatness with your cavalier attitude. You want the accolades of a hero without having to perform the heroic deeds, my friend. I never let up on a case and I rarely lose one as a result!"

McCarthy ducked his head in embarrassment at Shane's candid assessment and redirected his attention to the case. Whitmore's refusal to admit to statements he had made to Shane was a major topic. Shane was worried that they might see other witnesses do the same when it came time for them to testify. Their discussion ended when they climbed into their separate cars and both drove off, heading to Salamanca.

Shane went to the office and went over all the notes and files for the case. He hoped to figure out what The Colonel's strategy might be on Wednesday so that he could derail it. He arrived home at midnight to a darkened house. His wife woke, kissed him on the cheek and dropped her head back onto her pillow when he came to bed.

The Colonel tossed and turned all night. For the first time since Freddy's arrest he was worried about getting a conviction for first-degree murder. His resolve to obtain that conviction, however, remained unshaken.

CHAPTER TWELVE

THE PROSECUTION AND THE DEFENSE ENTERED THE COURTROOM shortly before ten o'clock on Wednesday, April 3, 1935 for day three of Freddy Lindsay's trial for the murder of Bernice Kenyon Farnsworth. Colonel Krieger and defense counsel Shane and McCarthy were primed for a contentious day in court.

The courtroom filled rapidly after the arrival of Lynn Blessing and the press pool. For many of the spectators, this was their first day in attendance; as a result, the courtroom buzzed with their excitement and anticipation.

Freddy made his entrance into the courtroom just as the spectators were settling into their seats. He was accompanied by his usual entourage of two sheriff's deputies and the court bailiff. He sat down at the defense table and the deputies took their seats flanking him. He cast his head down and did not look up for anyone other than Shane and McCarthy. Although Freddy could not see them, he again felt the penetrating stares of the spectators sitting behind him, which made him extremely anxious. He wanted to get up and leave the courtroom. Freddy honestly did not care about the outcome of the trial and he did not participate unless Shane or McCarthy forced him to do so. He knew the jury would return a guilty verdict. And in a strange sort of way, he welcomed that verdict. Freddy was slowly connecting with what he had done to Bernice and Harry Farnsworth.

Judge Larkin entered the courtroom shortly after ten o'clock and, referring to the county clerk's paperwork, verbally noted for the record that the jury, the alternate juror, and the defendant were present. Seeing that everything was in order, he opened the court for the day. The crowd went silent as they turned their complete attention towards The Colonel.

Sylvester Nodler was recalled for the State and he took the stand after being reminded he was still under oath. Without any objection from the defense, The Colonel introduced two photos he had overlooked during Nodler's examination on Tuesday. When he turned the witness over to the defense, Shane was quick with his cross-examination. He asked only for the time that both pictures were taken. Nodler was excused when The Colonel had no redirect.

Nora Moynihan was called to testify for the State, but she was unavailable. She had informed the clerk that she was too ill with the flu to testify that day. The Colonel then called for Dr. Hillsman, the surgeon who performed the autopsy of Bernice's body, to take the stand. The clerk stated that the doctor, too, was unable to appear because he was in the middle of surgery at the hospital. The Colonel silently prayed that Fred Houlihan would be present when he called for him to take the stand. Houlihan was in the hallway, and was escorted into the courtroom by the bailiff, who then swore him in.

Meticulously, The Colonel established that Fred Houlihan had a garage in Steamburg and that both Harry Farnsworth and Freddy Lindsay had frequented it often for the two months prior to the murders in Coldspring. Houlihan testified that he had seen Harry for the last time on the afternoon of Tuesday, March 5. He testified that Leon Johnson and Robert Deppa had been present when Freddy Lindsay sat sulking by the woodstove in the Houlihan garage that day.

Houlihan said he overheard part of the conversation between Harry and Freddy after Harry arrived with Bernice. Houlihan had been pumping five gallons of gasoline into the Sport Coupe. He testified that he heard Freddy refuse to return to the farm that afternoon. He said Harry left to buy Freddy some Duke's Mixture tobacco at Burr's store, located next door to his garage.

Houlihan was asked if he had identified the car in the jailhouse yard yesterday and if it was the same car he had serviced for the Farnsworth. He said it was the same vehicle.

Shane was quick to raise objections against the form of the State's questions. He was tired of The Colonel's leading questions and intended to put a stop to them. The judge sustained his objections immediately. When The Colonel moved on with the questioning, Shane popped up again and objected to the manner in which the questions were phrased. He claimed The Colonel's questions were either leading or vague. The initial examination of Fred Houlihan was concluded when he stated that Harry and Bernice Farnsworth drove off that afternoon, leaving Freddy to find his way back to Coldspring on his own power.

Syd Shane took up cross-examination of Houlihan and established that he had vouched for Harry Farnsworth's IOU purchases at Jacquay's grocery store, located across the street from Burr's general store. Harry had told him he was waiting for their milk check to come from the milk plant in Steamburg.

Shane became noticeably agitated when Houlihan's testimony contradicted statements he had given to McCarthy earlier the week prior in an interview at the garage in Steamburg. Unlike Shane who relied on his own notes, McCarthy had brought a stenographer with him on interviews and she had taken down Houlihan's every word. Houlihan stated in court that Tuesday, March 5, was the last day that he had seen Harry and Bernice Farnsworth.

"Mr. McCarthy called upon you at Steamburg for the purpose of interviewing you. Isn't that correct?" asked Shane.

"Yes," replied Houlihan.

"He had a stenographer with him, did he not?"

"Yes, sir."

"And did he tell you that he wanted the truth from you about the case?"

"Yes, sir."

"And did you tell him what you knew about the case?"

"Yes, sir."

"And while he was talking to you, was a stenographer taking down the questions and answers?"

"Yes, sir."

"And did you say at that time that Harry Farnsworth was there by himself on Monday and that Freddy Lindsay was there on Tuesday?"

"No."

"You did not say that?"

"No. Not Tuesday, no."

"So what you are saying is that there is a glaring error in the notes in the stenographer's transcription of your conversation with Mr. McCarthy?"

"Yes, sir."

Shane hoped the jurors were paying close enough attention to understand that not one, but two witnesses had changed statements recorded by an impartial stenographer. He tried to establish that there was another discrepancy concerning the day Freddy spent the afternoon in the garage, but Houlihan could not corroborate the facts of that situation. Houlihan was excused from the stand when Shane completed his questioning.

The People called Jay Stevens to the stand. Stevens established that he was employed as a lineman for the power company and that he did not know the Farnsworths. He stated he had seen Freddy several times in Houlihan's garage at Steamburg. He also testified that Freddy sat in the garage on Tuesday, March 5 and not Monday, March 4. Stevens did not have much else to offer. On cross-examination he stuck to his testimony about the day he saw Freddy Lindsay and Harry and Bernice Farnsworth at the garage. He did not hear any of their conversation.

Shane had no luck getting Stevens to admit he had the wrong

date at the garage, and his examination of the witness was short. Stevens was excused from the stand when Shane completed his questioning.

Leon Johnson took the stand next. Upon questioning, Johnson stated he had been in Houlihan's Garage on Tuesday. He also insisted that the day in question was Tuesday and not Monday. He had not heard or seen Harry and Bernice Farnsworth that day. He testified that Robert Deppa and John Monroe were present at the garage at the time in question.

On cross-examination Johnson testified he was in Houlihan's Garage on both Monday, March 4 and Tuesday, March 5. He was excused when Shane finished questioning him.

The next witness to testify was Robert Deppa, also a lineman for the power company, who had been in the garage with Jay Stevens and other witnesses. He testified that he saw Freddy Lindsay there on Tuesday afternoon. He, too, did not hear any of the conversations between the Farnsworths and Freddy Lindsay.

Judge Larkin had to step in at one point and assist The Colonel in obtaining testimony he was attempting to retrieve from Deppa. The Colonel was beginning to come apart at the seams. He was having a difficult time with the management of Freddy's trial. This case was by far the most complex case he had ever handled, and the absence of Nora Moynihan and Dr. Hillsman interrupted the systematic process he had devised for testimony. The Colonel's examination of Deppa ended when he stated he saw Freddy Lindsay at Houlihan's Garage on Tuesday, March 5.

Syd Shane sat at the defense table and shook his head in wonder at The Colonel's strategy. Too much time, in Shane's opinion, was being spent of establishing that Freddy Lindsay had sat in Houlihan's Garage on Tuesday, March 5 instead of Monday, March 4. He sighed as he stood to question the date with yet another of the State's witnesses. It was apparent to Shane that someone had influenced these men to cause them to deny the statements made to Mac McCarthy and him. Shane decided to get to the root of the problem when he began his cross-examination of Robert Deppa.

He established immediately that Deppa had spent both Monday and Tuesday in Houlihan's Garage, although Deppa stated he needed to consult his time sheets to be sure he was there on those days. Shane grilled Deppa in an attempt to trip him up, but Deppa remained calm and stuck to his testimony. The Colonel did not redirect with Deppa and the witness was excused.

John Monroe, a farmer from Coldspring, was called to the stand next. He gave testimony concerning a visit he made to the Farnsworth farm the week prior to the murder. Harry had advertised a couple of cows for sale and Monroe went there to see the animals. He headed for the Farnsworth property, but on the way his car got stuck in the mud on McGraw Road. Monroe said he walked a short distance to the Farnsworth farm, where he encountered Bernice, who was reluctant to lend him a shovel so that he could dig his car out of the mud. Then he said Bernice admitted later she'd been nervous about Monroe because she did not know him.

Shane jumped up. "Now, just a minute! I do not see where this testimony is relevant at all!"

Judge Larkin agreed. "I do not see any importance in this testimony!"

The Colonel stammered and made a feeble attempt to justify his questioning of Monroe, but gave up and turned the witness over to Shane. The trial was slipping out of his grip. Monroe's testimony was absolutely without merit.

Monroe was cross-examined by Shane and he testified that he was in Houlihan's Garage on Tuesday at the time the previous witnesses, Robert Deppa, stated he saw Freddy there. Monroe said he had not seen Freddy Lindsay in the garage at the time the other witnesses placed him there on Tuesday. Unfortunately for the

Defense, he was also in the garage on Monday and did not see Freddy on that date either. Monroe was excused after Shane concluded his examination.

After a short recess, The Colonel recalled Coroner George Middleton to the stand. Middleton's testimony established the time of his arrival at the Farnsworth farmhouse on Friday, March 8, and the presence of others already on the scene when he arrived. When Middleton was shown pictures of the interior of the farmhouse he stated that nothing had been moved prior to the photos being taken by Sylvester Nodler. The Colonel turned Middleton over to the Defense and Shane declined to question him. However, after Judge Larkin asked the coroner for clarification, The Colonel abruptly decided to redirect his examination of Middleton and showed the coroner the crime scene photo of Bernice lying in the cellar. The coroner emphasized that the photos of Bernice and the ones previously shown displayed the rooms in the exact same state as they had been when the bodies were discovered.

Middleton was visibly hostile towards Shane on recross-examination. But Shane led him gently when offering two photos taken of the dining room from different angles. Shane pointed out a dining chair that sat near a distinctive wicker chair in both photos, but then produced a third one.

"Do you see the chair I referred to as a dining chair in this picture?" asked Shane.

Middleton answered tersely, "I do not."

"It is apparent, is it not, that the chair that was sitting behind the wicker chair at the time that People's Exhibit 8 was taken was moved before People's Exhibit 10 was taken?"

Middleton glanced over at The Colonel and then back again at Shane and said, "I fail to see it in the picture."

Shane was unsuccessful in numerous attempts to get the coroner to admit that the chair had been moved. Middleton claimed a partition had hidden the chair from view. He used the same explanation for the missing chair when presented with another photo that should have contained the chair.

On redirect, The Colonel was unable to overcome the fact that Middleton's testimony concerning movement of objects in the house had been destroyed by Shane. He gave up abruptly as Shane raised objections to each of his questions for the coroner. Middleton stepped down and again left the courtroom in a dramatic huff.

Dr. Marshall Hillsman, who had just arrived at the courthouse, was called next for the State. Through a series of questions The Colonel established that Hillsman had obtained his medical degree from the University of Buffalo in 1911 and was currently licensed to practice medicine by the State of New York. He testified that he spent his internship at the Moses Taylor Hospital in Lackawanna for a year and a half before taking up practice in Cattaraugus County. After these preliminary questions, Hillsman testified about the autopsies he performed on Harry and Bernice's bodies on the evening of Friday, March 8.

He stated that Harry Farnsworth's body had most likely lay in the house for two or three days and described its post-mortem lividity. Ensuing questions asked him to describe the wounds to Harry's head and the powder burns around the wound over his right eyebrow. Hillsman also noted that the eyelashes and eyebrow of Harry's right eye had been burned away.

As his testimony continued, Hillsman related the discovery of two flattened bullets that had not penetrated Harry's skull. These bullets were found at the base of the skull and Harry's forehead. He described his discovery of the fatal bullet that had entered through the left base of Harry's skull and traveled through his brain. Hillsman's testimony went on for five more minutes before Judge Larkin called for a recess at half past twelve.

The Court reconvened at two o'clock and Hillsman finished

his testimony concerning the results of Harry's autopsy. The Colonel then moved on to Bernice Kenyon Farnsworth's autopsy. The jury, which had been noticeably bored with the doctor's testimony concerning Harry, perked up at the mention of Bernice's name.

Slowly the doctor described Bernice's physical attributes and admitted that he had known her by sight when she was alive and working at the courthouse. He remarked that her body displayed very little post-mortem lividity. He then described the condition of her body, beginning with her head.

"The face showed a laceration above the right eye about two inches long, running from the midline, just above the eyebrow and the base of the nose, outward to the right. About an inch above that was another laceration an inch in length. The two-inch laceration showed that the eyeball and the tissue attaching it to the roof of the orbit had been separated and the eyeball was placed downward. The pupil was dilated. The other eyeball was contracted. The nasal bones were shattered opposite the inner angle of the nose. The skin was not broken."

"At what point, doctor?" interrupted The Colonel. "Indicate to us, will you please, at what point was the nasal bone shattered?"

"Right about where the glasses rest on the nose."

"Well, continue. Tell us about that injury before you go on to another."

"We separated the soft tissues from the back area of the head, from the forehead over to the back of the head, and when those soft tissues were pulled aside it revealed a fracture running from the inner angle of the left eye slightly curving up and out to the right, over the right eye and over near the temporal bone. The fracture ran from the inner angle here, of the left eye, curving up over the forehead about three and one half inches long. And there was another fracture beginning about an inch to the right of the median line and at the fracture described, beginning and running irregularly backward and upward to the left over the vault of the skull. A fracture of eleven or twelve inches long. The fracture ran almost horizontal across the front bone and was not depressed."

"You mean not crushed like an eggshell?"

"No, just broken, and the two sides of the fracture were on an even plane. One was not knocked in below the other, not depressed."

"And do I understand you that the skull was actually parted by whatever caused the fracture?"

"Actually parting the head here, fracture resulting from a direct blow, and a fracture running back in what we what we term a bursting fracture."

"That is, not simply cracked, you mean?"

"No, but a bursting fracture. From the blow in front, the anteroposterior diameter of the skull cavity was shortened and the skull had to open to allow for that and it gave what we call a bursting fracture, extending back along the line of least resistance and in the direction of the force applied, which was backward and to the left."

The doctor then described the blood that had seeped under the scalp from the fracture and testified that, in his opinion, the injury to the skull was caused by one blow.

"You found another wound on the body, doctor?" asked The Colonel.

There was a slight commotion in the audience as Lynn Blessing stood up abruptly and jostled through the spectators on his way down the aisle. He exited the courtroom through the center aisle and did not return before court was recessed that evening.

"Yes," answered the doctor, "on the left side of the neck just above the line where the neck joins the shoulder, just into the neck. There was a wide-open wound four inches across from the anterior angle to the posterior angle. Exploring this wound, we found all of the tissues, namely the skin and the muscles, the jugular vein and the common carotid artery, the pneumogastric nerve, and the windpipe or trachea severed entirely, and also the esophagus, which is the swallowing tube, entirely severed. And then the wound went back and in toward the right side of the body, completely severing the cervical vertebra of the spinal column and the spinal cord. I would say the head was cut two-thirds from the body."

"Doctor, can you state which of these blows, if either, was the cause of death?"

"I would say that the wound in the neck was the cause of death."

"Now, the other wound to the head, can you state whether or not that would cause death?"

"I can."

"In how long a time?"

"Within a half hour is about the limit."

"And the wound in the neck would cause death within how long after its infliction?"

"I would say two minutes."

Hillsman, prompted by questions from The Colonel, stated that Bernice was standing when she received the blow to the head and in a prone position when she received the blow to her neck. He said if she had been standing when she received the blow to the neck, her clothing would have been drenched with the blood that would have spurted from her severed carotid artery. He testified that there was no blood-drench on her clothing, clearly indicating that she was lying on the ground when she received the killing blow or blows to her neck.

Satisfied with the description of the wounds to Bernice's body, The Colonel began another line of questioning. "From your examination of the two wounds that you have described, doctor, can you state with reasonable certainty what kind of instrument caused either or both of these injuries?"

"Yes, an axe," Hillsman replied.

The Colonel walked to the left side of the courtroom and momentarily disappeared from view. When he reappeared, he held the axe that had been used to kill Bernice. Freddy shuddered violently when he saw it. He let out a plaintive moan and began to sob. He buried his face in his handkerchief then tipped backwards in his chair as if he were about to faint. The courtroom spectators were riveted, seeing his reaction. Every eye in the jury was fixed on Freddy as he buried his head in his arms on the table. His muffled sobs could be clearly heard throughout the courtroom. No one spoke as Shane and McCarthy frantically attempted to calm their client. Judge Larkin ordered a minute's recess in the hope it would allow Freddy enough time to get a hold on himself.

A minute or so later, Shane announced that his client was sufficiently calm to continue with the trial. The judge reconvened the court.

With just one look, Shane and McCarthy communicated that Freddy's outburst had delivered a devastating blow to their defense. If the trial had ended at that moment, not one member of the jury would have had any doubt about Freddy's guilt in the charge of first-degree murder. But Shane and McCarthy were determined to move forward.

After The Colonel entered the axe into evidence, Doctor Hillsman testified that the axe in question could certainly have been used to inflict both wounds on Bernice's body. The Colonel ended his questioning of Hillsman.

On cross-examination, Shane began with a brief assault on Coroner Middleton's testimony concerning gunpowder residue on Harry's arm. Middleton had testified that he had observed spent gunpowder on Harry's left forearm. Doctor Hillsman testified that there was no gunpowder residue on Harry's arm at the time of the autopsy. Shane ended his examination of the doctor after establishing Harry's height, weight and muscle development. The doctor was excused from the stand without any redirect from The Colonel.

The courtroom buzzed when The Colonel called his star witness, Nora Moynihan, to the stand. Nora was the only witness who had spent significant time with Freddy Lindsay on March 4. She had shown up at the courthouse just after one o'clock, stating she was well enough to testify that afternoon.

For the benefit of the jury, The Colonel established that Nora was a neighbor to Bernice Kenyon when she lived in the log cabin on Price's Corner's Road. Nora said she remained in frequent contact with Bernice after she married Harry Farnsworth and moved to the McGraw Farm. The Colonel moved quickly to a visit Nora made to see the Farnsworths on February 24. Nora described Freddy as being uncommunicative for the entire three-and-a-half hours of her visit. However, when asked, she said she did not discuss Freddy's sullen behavior that day with Bernice.

Nora Moynihan's testimony turned out to be radically different from the testimony she gave on the same subject during her Grand Jury examination just two weeks earlier, on March 20. And for some reason, The Colonel did not seem to take notice of this about-face. Because the Grand Jury testimony was under seal, Syd Shane was unaware of the discrepancies.

Nora forgot she was not allowed to speak of conversations she'd had with anybody other than Freddy Lindsay. Shane repeatedly had to rise to object to her statements about what somebody had said and even to what she thought was on their mind. To make matters worse, The Colonel was focusing on mundane matters that had little merit to the case on trial.

After struggling through testimony about the delivery of three cans of water from the Farnsworths on the morning of March 4, The Colonel finally moved to Freddy's appearance at Nora's farm that day.

"And when and where did you see him?" asked The Colonel.

"Coming down the road toward my house," Nora answered.

"From which way?"

"From the direction of the McGraw Farm."

"What time do you think that was when you saw the defendant coming down the road?"

"Around ten o'clock, about that."

"Did the defendant stop at your house?"

"He did."

"You may describe anything he did or said."

"He walked right in without invitation and sat down."

"Was he in the habit of doing that?"

"No, that was the first time Freddy had ever come there and walked in alone. He mentioned that he had what little clothes he had and said Mrs. Farnsworth asked him what Mr. Farnsworth went to the barn to get."

"Do you mean Lindsay told you this on Monday morning?"

"Yes, and he said he didn't answer readily and so Mrs. Farnsworth asked him again and he said he spoke up a little bit loud. And she said, 'You are not to talk to me like that, young man. This is my place, my investment, and I should know what is to be repaired or what is going on.' And that is as much as he told me what happened."

"Did he have his clothes with him?"

"Yes, he did."

Nora then described the clothing she saw in a paper sack Freddy had carried into her house. The Colonel produced a paper sack that had been retrieved from Bernice's Sport Coupe in New York City. He entered the sack into evidence after Nora positively identified it as the same sack she had seen in Freddy's possession at her house on March 4. Then she described the few chores Freddy performed for her, and the vegetable dinner she had served to him at noon, just before he left for Houlihan's Garage in

Steamburg.

The examination of Nora Moynihan moved on to the return of the Farnsworths at three o'clock that same day when they drove her to and from a neighbor's house to get lamp oil.

"Then after the Farnsworths left, you saw this defendant again?" The Colonel asked.

"Yes."

"Where?"

"He came back."

"To your house?"

"Yes."

"And what day of the week do you place that, Monday or Tuesday?"

"Monday."

"And he was on foot?"

"Yes."

"Did you have any further conversation with him then?"

"Yes. He said he had talked with the Farnsworths at Steamburg."

"And did he say anything else?"

"He said they wanted him to return and I said, 'Are you going to?' and he shook his head."

"Shook his head?"

"In the negative."

Nora described the chores Freddy performed for her that afternoon in exchange for a light supper. She testified that he left her house at about 7:30 that evening and walked in the direction of Steamburg. Then she stated that she left her house at 9:30 to visit a neighbor and returned home sometime after ten o'clock.

The Colonel then asked Nora about a set of keys to Nora's brother's house, just down the road from her. He intended to show that Freddy had stolen the keys from Nora along with other articles while she was out visiting her neighbor that evening.

When he instructed Nora to tell the court everything she knew about the keys, Syd Shane shot out of his seat with an objection.

"That is objected to, Your Honor," Shane said to the judge.

"Well, I do not see the competency of this," replied Judge Larkin, looking directly at The Colonel.

"If Your Honor please," argued The Colonel, "I propose to show where the defendant stayed Monday night."

"All right, if she knows where he stayed," the judge said agreeably.

"This witness does not, Your Honor," said The Colonel in a quiet tone.

"She what?" shouted the judge.

"She can identify some of her personal property."

"Well, let her identify it, but I do not think this is competent evidence. The testimony is coming pretty close to proving an independent crime not in any way connected to this case."

The Colonel produced a small clock Nora identified as belonging to her, but she could not say with any certainty when she had last seen the clock. Shane objected that Nora was unresponsive with her answers to the District Attorney. The Colonel ignored Shane's objection and asked the judge to have the clock marked for identification and entered in as evidence.

"I still do not see the force of this testimony!" the judge said hotly as the bailiff marked the clock as evidence.

Reluctantly, Judge Larkin allowed The Colonel to continue having Nora identify her personal property. When The Colonel brought out a lantern Nora identified as hers, it was entered into evidence. The Colonel produced an earthenware water jug and Nora testified that it belonged to her.

"Did there come a time that you missed the jug?" asked The Colonel.

"It stood where I saw it all winter and I missed it," she replied.

"When did you miss it?"

"During that week. I began to look around and missed the lantern and the jug."

Shane threw his pencil down on the table and rose once again to object to the testimony being given by Nora Moynihan. He wanted to know where The Colonel was going with his line of questioning.

"If Your Honor, please," Shane said with obvious irritation, "I am going to object to this again on the ground that there is no connection."

In agreement with Shane, Judge Larkin said, "I still do not see the force of this, but I will let her show when she missed it. It has not been connected up to this point at all."

The questioning about the water jug resumed, but after Nora answered the first question, Shane shot up again and objected. The Colonel had clearly misstated one of Nora's responses when he re-iterated it to her. The objection was sustained.

Mysteriously, The Colonel produced two blankets and asked Nora to identify them. She stated they were her blankets that went missing on Monday, March 4. The blankets were marked as evidence. Next up for display was an empty glove box. Nora identified it as belonging to her and The Colonel entered the box into evidence. The judge shook his head but allowed The Colonel to continue with his questioning of the witness.

The Colonel returned to the subject of her brother's house keys. Once again Shane rose to object to the line of questioning. "If Your Honor please," he said, "I renew my objection! It is obvious that the only purpose of this testimony is to try to prove some independent crime. If the purpose of the testimony is to show that the defendant stayed in the house of her brother on the night previous to March 5, there is no necessity of putting this stuff in evidence. We are willing to stipulate that and concede that. The only purpose I can see for putting this evidence in is to poison the jury!"

Judge Larkin directed his comments at The Colonel. "I am going to sustain Mr. Shane's objection and before you go much further, the statement you have from the defendant should be put into evidence. I have admitted proof here upon the theory that there are admissions or statements therein contained which render competent evidence. This evidence certainly is not competent in the way in which you are putting it in and I instruct the jury to disregard all of her testimony, everything that she has testified to up to now. I do not see any relevancy or materiality to anything that she has testified to in this lawsuit!"

An argument between Judge Larkin and Colonel Krieger ensued and the request for Freddy's statement was forgotten. The judge stipulated that only the testimony concerning the bedding, the clock, the water jug and the lantern be stricken from the record. When the judge allowed The Colonel to continue with his examination of Nora Moynihan, he walked back to the prosecution's table. The Colonel picked up his notes, then looked at Nora, who was patiently waiting on the witness stand. He glanced down again at his notes and cleared his throat. When he raised his head he turned to Shane and said quietly, "You may ask."

The spectators chattered loudly among themselves, wondering what had just taken place. Judge Larkin hammered his gavel and demanded silence. The bailiff advised the spectators that any further interruption would result in their immediate expulsion from the courtroom. The newspapermen in the front row scribbled furiously on their notepads.

Syd Shane sat and stared at The Colonel. Finally, he shook his head as if to clear it, and stood. He launched into a brilliant cross-examination of Nora Moynihan in the manner of a fox that waits patiently for the right moment to pounce on its prey. He lulled Nora into complacency by asking how long she had lived in her house. She responded easily when he asked about her farm and how many cows and chickens she maintained there. Then he moved on to her acquaintance with Bernice Farnsworth and established that Nora baked bread for the Farnsworths after they were married.

With expert ability, Shane effortlessly guided Nora through her acquaintance with Freddy Lindsay and her experience with him and Harry Farnsworth when they cut down a large maple tree for her in early February. Shane also established that Freddy had come by himself on another occasion to solder a milk can for her. When Shane asked Nora if she had ever shared a pot of tea with Freddy, she flatly denied it.

During Nora's examination by The Colonel, Freddy had whispered to Shane that he had visited Nora several times by himself and had tea with her. Shane didn't like Nora as a witness. He wondered about the possibility that she was determined see Freddy was convicted of first-degree murder. Meanwhile, Freddy was steadfast in his claim that Nora had given him her brother's keys and the rest of the articles that had been found in her brother's house on Friday, March 8.

Judge Larkin watched Shane closely as he continued his cross-examination. He had never seen Shane at work in a courtroom and he was very impressed.

Continuing, Shane asked about the movements of the Farnsworths and Freddy Lindsay to and from her house on Monday, March 4. Then he moved on to Freddy's appearance at her house that morning.

"You had finished emptying your milk cans before the defendant came to your porch, is that not so?" asked Syd.

"Yes, I think so," Nora replied.

"And who walked into the house first, you or he?"

"I think I did."

"And he came in behind you?"

"Yes."

"Now, you did not order him to leave, did you? You did not tell him to get out of your house?"

"No, I didn't think that was a good way to go."

"But you did not, in any event?"

"No."

"You did not indicate to him in any way that he was unwelcome?"

"That wouldn't be good policy."

"That is not what I asked you, Miss Moynihan! You did not indicate to him that he was unwelcome there?"

"No."

It seemed as though Nora finally understood that Shane was not going to tolerate her antics on the stand. She began responding to his questions with short 'yes' and 'no' answers instead of offering unsolicited information and opinions.

Nora established beyond a doubt that Monday, March 4 was the day Freddy came to her house and returned later after having visited Houlihan's Garage. When Nora verified the date, Shane turned and looked over at The Colonel to punctuate the clarification of a much-beleaguered bone of contention. He hoped The Colonel would finally give up his obsession with setting Tuesday, March 5 as the day Freddy's activity in Steamburg took place.

Much of the remainder of Shane's cross-examination of Nora clarified the testimony she had just given to the District Attorney. The line of questioning moved through the paper sack with Freddy's clothing, his statement concerning his decision to leave his job with the Farnsworths, and his activity in general during both of his visits to her house that Monday.

Shane finally unleashed a verbal attack on Nora when she stated that Freddy told her he was not going back to the Farnsworths. He pulled out a sheaf of papers that contained his own personal transcription of her conversation with him at her farm in late March. He was unsuccessful in getting Nora to admit that she had made any of the statements that were contradictory to that day's testimony.

When Shane questioned Nora about Freddy's demeanor in general, she was evasive. When her answers became unresponsive, he cut her off mid-sentence by repeating the question again. Nora became angry, then flustered. Eventually, however, Shane solved the mystery of the loaves of bread hanging on the mudroom door to the Farnsworth house.

Nora testified that it was she who had placed the bread there on Wednesday afternoon, March 6, after Bernice failed to collect them from her as agreed on Tuesday, March 5. Nora stated that she walked all around the house and looked in all the windows when she received no answer at the front door. She said she did not see Harry lying just inside the front door.

Before turning Nora back over to The Colonel, Shane requested that the court order Nora Moynihan to be available outside the courtroom for each of the remaining days of the trial in case he needed to cross-examine her again. Judge Larkin ordered her to do so and The Colonel rose to redirect.

The redirect examination was brief. The Colonel asked if Nora had seen a table with a lunch cloth on it from the dining room window of the farmhouse. He released her from the stand when she said she had seen the table in question. Judge Larkin reminded her to remain available for the duration of the trial.

Although it was early evening, Judge Larkin allowed the trial to continue. The Colonel then called Adam P. Walsh to the stand. Walsh was the patrolman from the 24th Police Precinct who had Bernice's abandoned Sport Coupe towed in New York City.

Walsh established that he had observed the Sport Coupe parked in front of a sixteen-family tenement house located at 983 Columbus Avenue on Wednesday, March 6 while walking his beat. He said that he wrote the license number on a note pad and that he kept on walking. He said that he saw the car again the next day while on patrol. When asked, Walsh testified that he ordered the removal of the car through a clerical patrolman at the end of his beat on Thursday, March 7. After Walsh testified that the car in the yard next to the courthouse was the same vehicle, The Colonel turned the patrolman over to Shane for cross-examination.

Shane's examination of the patrolman was brief and concerned only the testimony he had just given to the court. Walsh was excused when The Colonel did not redirect.

The final witness of the day was Detective Walter Clancy. Clancy gave testimony concerning the removal of the Sport Coupe from 983 Columbus Street and its subsequent shipment to Cattaraugus County. When The Colonel's focus shifted to the role Clancy had played in Freddy's arrest, Judge Larkin called for an adjournment until ten o'clock the next morning.

Everyone in the courtroom was exhausted. As soon as the judge retired through the back of the courtroom, the two deputies assigned to Freddy cuffed him and wasted no time hustling him out. In the meantime, Colonel Krieger made a beeline for the door and was gone before Syd Shane and Mac McCarthy packed their valises.

The spectators moved sluggishly as they exited the courtroom and made their way downstairs. The crowd in the lobby and on the courthouse lawn was a little thinner than the previous two days due to the late hour of adjournment.

Shane and McCarthy shared dinner again at the hotel where they quietly discussed the day's proceedings.

"What in the heck do you think Krieger was doing with all that stuff from Moynihan's house?" McCarthy asked Shane.

"Trying to use Freddy's supposed petty theft from Nora Moynihan as a testament to his poor character," Syd surmised. "Perhaps he's trying to make Freddy look like a cowardly thief who preys upon helpless women. And if that was the case, the

175

judge granted him enough leeway to accomplish just that. I think the jury figured out where The Colonel was going after he produced the blankets."

"Hmmm, you may be right. I don't know. What's on the agenda for tomorrow?"

"I think we'll see some heavy hitters on the stand tomorrow. That is, I think we'll be hearing from State Trooper George, Sheriff Carlson, Deputy Sheriff Pickup and the fingerprint expert from Jamestown, Elmer Lee. Lee is the most problematic witness we have coming up for testimony. He has Freddy's fingerprint on the cashbox. I don't think we'll be able to do anything to minimize his testimony. Somehow we've got to show that Freddy went back to the farm to collect his pay without the intention of stealing it from them."

After dinner, around eight o'clock, the two defense attorneys headed to Salamanca. Shane passed up his usual late evening office time and went directly home.

At The Colonel's house, you wouldn't have known he had been through a bad day in court. Conversation around the dinner table focused on the day's proceedings and talk of the trial continued until everyone retired for bed at ten o'clock.

Freddy ate a late supper and stretched out on his bed. The day's testimony had completely sapped his energy. He felt as though he had spent the day doing hard labor. The shock of seeing the axe in the courtroom had drained him. Visions of Bernice lying at his feet floated in and out of his mind. He could almost feel the rough axe handle in his hands and then the vision vanished completely.

Lynn Blessing sat in his easy chair in the living room of his house on River Street. He was mulling over ways to get out of attending tomorrow's session at the courthouse. After a while he concluded that there was no way out. Edith would insist he be there to represent Bernice's family in the courtroom.

The last of the shops in Little Valley closed their doors at the unusually late hour of nine o'clock. One by one the lights inside the shop windows on Main Street winked out as the owners locked up and left for home. By 9:30, Little Valley was transformed back into a peaceful hamlet for the remainder of the night.

CHAPTER THIRTEEN

APRIL 4, 1935, DAY FOUR OF FREDDY LINDSAY'S TRIAL FOR murder, began in much the same manner as it had on the previous three days. Sheriff Carlson, who was standing at the courtroom windows at 9:30 a.m., noted that the crowds were noticeably smaller that morning. He was grateful, as his staff was weary of controlling the huge crowds. His staff was also starting to crack under the stress of working mandatory double shifts. They had been doing so since Freddy's arrival at the jail on March 14.

Counsel for the People and the Defense were seated and waiting for Judge Larkin when the judge appeared promptly at ten o'clock. He asked and received County Clerk Guy Fargo's assurance that all thirteen jurors and the defendant were present. He reconvened the trial for the morning session.

Walter Clancy was recalled to the stand and The Colonel picked up his examination exactly where it had halted in yesterday's session. Clancy chronicled the events that took place when he and his partner, Detective Notheis, first noticed Freddy at Rector's Restaurant on Broadway in New York City on March 11.

"How did you happen to be there?" asked The Colonel.

"As a result of an assignment upon this case by Inspector McDermott, my superior officer," Clancy replied.

"And tell us about your going there to the restaurant and whom you saw there."

"While sitting at one of the tables, I observed the defendant walk up to a counter and order some food. It was a very hot day. The defendant had on a pair of kid gloves. He got the food, went to a table and sat there with the kid gloves on. Then he took them off under the table. The defendant bore a striking resemblance to a picture, which I had in my pocket, of his brother. I then got in a position where I could see the defendant's hands. I noticed on the back of his hands a tattoo mark. I waited until the defendant completed his eating and then followed him from the restaurant on Broadway to Forty-Sixth Street, where I walked up to the defendant in company with Detective Notheis, my partner, and I asked him if his name was Robert Lindsay. He said, 'No.' I said, 'You look very much like a man we want in a vice investigation in New York. 'Where do you come from?' He answered, 'Lower Massachusetts.' I said, 'What is your name?' He said, 'Flynn.' I said, 'You had better come with us to the stationhouse because we have someone there who can identify you.' He said, 'Not me because my name isn't Robert Lindsay.' We got in the car and while we were on our way to the station the defendant said, 'Have you really got someone in the station house that can identify Lindsay?' "

Freddy turned to Shane and McCarthy and whispered, "That's not how it happened at all! He's lying about almost everything. And they threw me against the wall and cuffed me!"

Shane whispered back, "Don't worry about it, Freddy. He's just covering for himself and his partner. Nothing he said has damaged you. Let it go. We want this man off the stand as soon as possible. Trust me on this, all right?"

Freddy looked Shane in the eye and shrugged his shoulders. "Okay," he whispered. "I trust you."

The Colonel interrupted Clancy and asked, "That was you and Notheis and the defendant?"

"Yes," replied Clancy. "I said, 'Yes.' He said, 'Who can identify Lindsay?' I said, 'A woman.' He said, 'Thank god for that because I am not Lindsay.' "

The detective went on to describe the kid gloves he saw Freddy remove from his hands at Rector's Restaurant. When The

179

Colonel produced the gloves, Clancy identified them as the same pair that he took from Freddy on the day of his arrest. The gloves were marked and entered in as evidence. The Colonel turned Clancy over to Syd Shane.

Freddy waved his hand to get Shane's attention but Shane waved it off and motioned for him to be patient. He rose from his chair and said, "No questions."

The spectator's soft murmur temporarily filled the courtroom as they waited for the next People's witness to enter and take the stand. Michael F. McDermott, Inspector in Charge of the New York City Third Detective District, was sworn in.

Under examination by The Colonel, McDermott chronicled the events relating to Freddy's arrest from the day they received the General Alarm teletype sent out on March 9 by State Trooper Lieutenant George. McDermott was the person who assigned detectives Clancy and Notheis to the Bob Lindsay/Broadway Theater robbery case and posted them for surveillance. McDermott provided the details of his questioning of Freddy after his arrival at the station. He spoke about Freddy's eventual admission that he was not the Lindsay they were looking for, but was his brother, Alfred Lindsay. He said that when Freddy was shown the photo McDermott had in his pocket, Freddy identified the person as his other brother, Leroy. McDermott was asked to identify Freddy Lindsay, sitting in the courtroom, as the same person he interviewed as Alfred J. Lindsay and he did so.

The rest of McDermott's testimony, which went on for another fifteen minutes, was read verbatim from his handwritten notes. He went through every detail Freddy provided beginning from the time he met Harry at Great Meadow Prison through his stay at the Farnsworth farm, what he could remember about the day of the murder, his flight to New York City and his visit to see his sisters, Helen and Mary. The Colonel ended his examination there and turned the witness over to the Defense.

Mac McCarthy rose from his seat and approached the witness. "Are those notes your own notes which you have there?"

"Yes," said McDermott.

"Do you object to showing them to me?"

"I don't think you have any right to see them. I will let the judge rule on that!"

"Let me see them," said Judge Larkin.

As the judge looked over McDermott's notes, McCarthy continued to question him.

"Those are in your own handwriting, are they?"

"Yes," McDermott said as he turned and addressed the bench. "Your Honor, I would like to be advised as to whether these are confidential notes taken by a police officer in an investigation and if so, I feel justified in not showing them."

"Of course," replied Judge Larkin. "You have referred to them in connection with your testimony. I assume that Mr. McCarthy is entitled to see them to determine if they actually did refresh your memory. You may show them to him."

McCarthy thanked the judge and took the notes from McDermott. Shane asked for a recess in order for him and McCarthy to have sufficient time to read the notes in their entirety. Judge Larkin granted them a short recess.

When court reconvened, Shane and McCarthy had not quite finished reading McDermott's notes. They agreed to allow The Colonel to redirect with McDermott while they continued reading.

On redirect, The Colonel tidied up a few more points about the Sport Coupe. He completed his questions when McDermott identified the registration slip from Bernice's car. The Colonel had the slip admitted into evidence.

McCarthy resumed his cross-examination and questioned the inspector about statements Freddy made referencing his throwing the gun out of the window of the car versus stopping, exiting the car and then throwing out the gun. McDermott said Freddy told him he threw the gun out of the car through the window. McCarthy ended his questions by asking how much money Freddy told him he had when he arrived in New York City. McDermott testified that Freddy told him he had eighty-five cents when he arrived in the city. McCarthy turned him back over to the State and The Colonel excused him.

The State called Sheriff Lester W. Carlson to the stand. After identifying who Sheriff Carlson was, The Colonel began to probe the sheriff about articles from the Farnsworth farm that he had taken into his personal possession. The items were a shovel found lying partially under the Airtight stove in the living room, a poker found near Harry's head, a metal cashbox with its lid pried open found near Harry's head, and another cashbox found in an upstairs bedroom. The sheriff identified each item from photos. The Colonel showed him and each one was entered in as evidence.

When the first cashbox was shown to the sheriff, it was apparent there were prints on it. When the second cashbox, filled with papers, was shown to him, it was revealed that the Defense knew nothing about what the box contained. After an objection by Shane, the judge agreed he would allow testimony from the sheriff about the box after the Defense had time to review its contents during the noon recess.

The sheriff affirmed the presence of the suitcase in the kitchen packed with men's clothes and the incubator and a lamp down in the cellar. With the exception of the suitcase, those items were entered as evidence when they were produced and identified by Carlson. The Colonel moved on to the axe and asked the sheriff to identify it as the same one that appeared in the photograph of Bernice lying in the basement. Carlson testified that the axe was in the same condition as when it had been found, except that the dried blood on the blade had turned dark.

Next, The Colonel questioned Carlson about his participation in the acquisition of a six-page statement by Freddy on the night of his return to Cattaraugus County. It was established that Colonel Krieger, Lieutenant George and Elmer Miller were present at the time of the questioning. When Freddy's statement was offered for evidence by the State, Shane objected and asked to be given time to read it. Although the statement had been published in several newspapers, Shane had to wait until it was offered as evidence in order to see the original document. Again, the judge instructed him to peruse the document during the noon recess. He allowed the statement to be marked and entered as evidence and then given to the Defense.

Judge Larkin had to admonish the spectators twice more when they broke into laughter after hearing Carlson's responses. "Just a moment!" he shouted. "Do you not realize what you are listening to? Laughter does not fit this scene at all. There is nothing humorous about this!"

The Colonel asked the sheriff about a search conducted near Olean done in the hopes of retrieving the gun Freddy threw into a field on March 5. Carlson testified that his deputies, several State Troopers, and a ten-man search team from Randolph were unable to locate the pistol in a three-quarter-mile sweep of the section of road identified by Freddy. The Colonel ended his examination there.

Syd Shane grilled Carlson about how Freddy's statement was taken and asked for the time and date that Freddy signed it. He asked about the location and position of the shovel at the crime scene. The sheriff became confused and contradicted himself several times when he was asked to locate and describe the position of other crime scene items without the benefit of crime scene photos. When laughter erupted yet again after the sheriff's response, Judge Larkin stood up and yelled across the room at the spectators.

"Is it going to be necessary for me to clear the courtroom? What is there about that answer that called for laughter?"

The bailiff warned them that one more outburst and the court would be cleared for the day. The spectators quieted down immediately and were visibly repentant for their actions.

When Shane finished with the articles that had been entered as evidence, he moved on. He asked a series of questions regarding the clearing of the house furnishings and personal objects prior to his visit there on March 21. Carlson vehemently denied that he had anything to do with the authorization of the clearing of the crime scene. He intimated that the authorization might have come from someone beneath him in his department. Shane ended his cross-examination there and announced that he might want to continue with the sheriff after he read Freddy's statement during the noon recess.

Colonel Krieger redirected his examination of the sheriff. One item lying on the State's table had been covered by The Colonel's papers. The Colonel asked Sheriff Carlson to identify a poker found near Harry's head and entered it into evidence. He ended his redirect when the sheriff identified Frances Chambers as the woman who had recorded the entire session that preceded the signing of Freddy's statement.

Shane, on recross, attempted again to have the sheriff identify the location of several items in the house. The sheriff was unable to correctly place them and Shane's recross was suspended when Judge Larkin called for the noon recess. He asked that everyone return at two o'clock.

Shane and McCarthy sent out for lunch and spent most of the noon recess in the courtroom going over Freddy's statement and the contents of the second cashbox.

When court resumed, Judge Larkin took up a matter of redacted testimony that needed both parties' approval. When that bit of business was done, Shane continued his recross-examination of Sheriff Carlson.

Shane quickly established that although Freddy's statement

was transcribed in a narrative form, it had not been given in the same form. The Colonel had drawn up the document as a narrative based on a cobbling of statements Freddy made to them. Sheriff Carlson became hostile and offered information that did not apply to the questions being asked of him. Shane moved on to the statement Freddy gave to The Colonel and Carlson finally admitted that the statement offered into evidence was not dictated by Freddy himself.

When Shane questioned the sheriff about the clearing out of furnishings from the Farnsworth farmhouse, Carlson became unresponsive and evasive. He would not admit that Freddy told him he knew Bernice did not keep any money in the house at any time. Shane ended his recross and The Colonel began his redirect.

Colonel Krieger obtained permission from the court to show Carlson the actual eighty-page transcript of the conversations they'd had with Freddy on March 14 in order to refresh the sheriff's memory. He asked Carlson to specifically read page fifty-nine.

"What is it? What do you have to say about it now, having read that?" The Colonel said.

"The question brought forth," replied Carlson, "was regarding the prying open of the money box, and Freddy said he did not pry it open because he knew there was no money around there, presumably meaning the box."

The Colonel rested.

On recross by Shane, Carlson admitted that Freddy's six-page statement had been boiled down from eighty pages of transcripts. The Defense rested and The Colonel did not redirect.

The State then called State Trooper Lieutenant William J. George to the stand. After questions that identified him to the jury, Lieutenant George gave testimony that placed him at the farmhouse on March 8. He identified all the personnel present at the location and was shown all of the photographs that had been entered in as evidence. When Lieutenant George finished looking at the photos, he stated he was present when all but two were taken. The Colonel then asked him about the condition of the kitchen at the time of his arrival. The lieutenant testified that he saw a pan of water and a coffee pot with coffee in it on the kitchen stove. He described two milk pails that stood in front of the stove. He noted that the kitchen table was set with two plates, two knives, two cups and two saucers. A cake sat in the center of the table. The Colonel then asked him about the suitcase at the back door to the kitchen.

Lieutenant George stated the suitcase contained men's clothing and a man's leather jacket. He explained that the suitcase was closed and returned to its original location. He recalled when Elmer Lee arrived and began fingerprinting the objects in the house.

The remainder of The Colonel's examination centered on Lieutenant George's trip to New York City to retrieve Freddy and what occurred after their return to Cattaraugus County. The Colonel asked about the day Freddy was interrogated for the statement he signed for the District Attorney. Lieutenant George spoke of corrections Freddy made to the first draft of the statement before signing it. In response to The Colonel's final question, Lieutenant George testified that no one under any circumstances used force or false promises to pressure Freddy into signing the statement.

On cross-examination, Lieutenant George testified that a photograph of the kitchen was not taken by Nodler. Shane then had the lieutenant provide details regarding the contents of the pans found on the stove. Shane ended his examination when the lieutenant listed all the people present during Freddy's interrogation that resulted in his signed statement. The Colonel declined to redirect.

The next witness called for the People was Alfred Carpenter, a receiving clerk employed at the Queensboro Dairy Products Company in Steamburg. Carpenter testified that he last saw Harry Farnsworth on Tuesday March 5 when Harry dropped off seventy pounds of milk at the milk plant. The Colonel ended his examination when Carpenter stated that Harry did not come to the plant with milk on Wednesday.

On cross-examination, Carpenter testified he was unsure when farmers were paid by the plant for their milk. His testimony ended when he stated Harry Farnsworth had asked him if his check had come in and Carpenter had told him, no, it had not. Carpenter stepped down from the stand after The Colonel did not take up a redirect.

The Colonel called Beatrice Cain to the stand. She was the bookkeeper at the Queensboro milk plant. Cain testified that her record sheet showed Harry Farnsworth had dropped off seventy-one pounds of milk at the plant on Tuesday, March 5. She also testified that Harry did not pick up the milk check that came for him at the plant on Monday, March 4. The Colonel ended his examination of Cain when she stated again that Harry's last milk delivery was on March 5.

Shane asked only one question of Cain: was milk accepted at night as well as in the morning? Cain responded that she did not know and she was excused from the stand.

Ethel Zimmerman was called next by the People. Zimmerman was a teller at the Salamanca Trust Company. She testified that Bernice had come in on February 25 and withdrawn one hundred thirty seven dollars and eighty-five cents from her account. Zimmerman produced the original check that Bernice had presented to the bank for that amount. The Colonel had it entered as evidence and ended his examination. Zimmerman was excused from the stand without any cross-examination by the Defense.

The courtroom came alive when Jerome A. Crowley was called and sworn in as the next witness for the People. Crowley was the prominent President of the State Bank of Randolph. He testified that Harry Farnsworth opened a joint checking account with a cash deposit of one hundred thirty dollars on February 25. The Colonel turned Crowley over to the Defense.

Shane asked Crowley for the current balance on the new account after a check for one dollar and fifty cents had been honored. Crowley stated that the account currently stood at one-hundred twenty-eight dollars and fifty cents. For The Colonel's redirect, Crowley produced the original ledger showing Harry's new account balance, and then he was excused.

Ira Bennett was recalled by The Colonel for the sole purpose of giving testimony about his discovery of two milk cans found on the side of McGraw Road. He stated that he took the cans to the Farnsworth barn, where they were examined later that day by Deputy Sheriff Leone Pickup. Bennett was given a photograph taken by Sylvester Nodler and he identified the spot where he found the cans.

Mac McCarthy cross-examined Ira Bennett and determined that the cans were found on Sunday, March 10. When questioned about the date of the pictures, Ira was unsure what day they had been taken. After one redirect and one recross that produced little new information, Ira was excused.

The next witness called for the People was Deputy Leone B. Pickup. After giving testimony that identified him as the man-in-charge at the Sheriff's Office on Friday, March 8, The Colonel led him through the same set of questions he had asked Lieutenant George. Pickup located various items in the kitchen and then testified that he left the crime scene and performed investigations in Coldspring and Randolph until 6:30 that evening.

Upon request, Pickup examined all the photos in evidence and vouched for their accuracy. The Colonel had him identify the poker, knife, two cashboxes, and a white knit cap with blackened holes. The Colonel then asked him to identify the location of

Bernice's body and the axe. Pickup did so using the cellar stairs as a reference.

"What did you notice in the appearance of the axe?" said The Colonel.

"It was blood-stained."

"Wet or dry?"

"Dry."

"Can you identify if this is that axe?" The Colonel handed the axe to Leone, who inspected it carefully.

"It is," Pickup answered.

"How did you identify it?"

"By the blades and the bloodstains."

"What about the blades?"

"One blade has a keen edge and the other is nicked."

"Does it appear to be in the same condition now as when you first saw it in the Farnsworth cellar?"

"Yes, sir."

"Is the color as pronounced, whatever it is on the blade, as it was then?"

"Yes, sir."

"Did you notice anything on Mrs. Farnsworth's body?"

"I did not."

"Or anything that looked like blood?"

"I did not."

"Was there any blood on her face?"

"No, sir."

The Colonel then addressed Harry Farnsworth's autopsy. Pickup testified he had been present during the autopsy and that Dr. Hillsman had handed him three bullets one-by-one as they were removed from Harry's head. He identified the glass vial with the flattened bullet from the right side of Harry's head and it was entered as evidence. The Colonel produced another glass vial with a flattened bullet taken from above the right eyebrow on Harry's head. It, too, was identified by Pickup and entered as evidence. The Colonel produced a third vial with a bullet in it.

"I show you this other vial, Mr. Pickup. Is that the other bullet?" The Colonel asked.

"Yes, sir."

"Were you there when Dr. Hillsman extracted it?"

"I was."

"From where was it extracted?"

"From the brain."

"And did you see what part of the brain he got it out of?"

"Yes, sir."

"Did you see where there was a hole in the side of the skull?"

"I did."

"And what side of the head did this bullet come out of in reference to the side that the hole was on?"

"The opposite side."

Syd Shane and The Colonel wrangled over the admission of Pickup's testimony concerning the presence of powder marks on Harry's body. When Judge Larkin overruled Shane's objection, Pickup stated that he observed a circle of black specks on Harry's forearm. When the line of questioning addressed the milk cans Ira Bennett found on McGraw Road, Shane and The Colonel wrangled again. Shane did not want them admitted as evidence because they had not been clearly identified. The judge reached the end of his patience with The Colonel's steady stream of unproductive fishing expeditions.

Judge Larkin stood, placed his hands palms down upon the bench, leaned forward and called out to the audience in an exasperated tone, "Is there anyone here from the milk plant who can identify these as their cans?"

Alfred Carpenter, who had testified earlier and had taken the only empty seat in the courtroom, stood and announced cheerily, "I can!"

Judge Larkin beckoned Carpenter to approach the bench. Deputy Sheriff Pickup was confused. He didn't know what to do.

The Colonel waved his hands at Pickup and said, "Will you get down off the stand, please!"

Pickup jumped up from the witness chair and took Carpenter's seat in the audience. Shane was amused by the unconventional proceeding but did not object to the recall of Carpenter to the stand.

Judge Larkin reminded Alfred Carpenter that he was still under oath and The Colonel began his examination by asking Carpenter if he recognized the milk cans.

Carpenter responded by offering unsolicited information about all the milk cans being marked. Shane leapt up from his seat and objected on the grounds that the witness was unresponsive in his answer.

Judge Larkin rolled his eyes back as if to say, 'Oh, no! Not again!' and took matters into his own hands once more.

"Mr. Carpenter, go over and look at those cans and see if you know where those cans came from or to whom they belong!"

Carpenter walked over to where the cans had been placed, checked the numbers stamped into them, and returned to the stand. "We go by their number. Farnsworth's number is three-ninety-eight, listed on the records."

"And is that can numbered three-ninety-eight?" asked The Colonel, pointing at one of the milk cans.

"Three-ninety-eight," agreed Carpenter.

"And what is the number of the other can?"

"Three-ninety-eight."

Just to make certain, Judge Larkin himself questioned Carpenter to be sure this testimony would not be re-visited again. He asked Carpenter to positively identify the two milk cans as cans belonging to Harry Farnsworth.

The Colonel ended his examination with a strange question.

"Mr. Carpenter, did you know Farnsworth by any particular nickname?"

"I did not."

"Do you know whether or not he bore the nickname of 'Doc'?"

"Not to my knowledge."

"You never heard him called by any nickname?"

"No."

"You may cross-examine."

Syd Shane asked Carpenter if he knew that Harry had picked up those cans on Tuesday, March 5. He said he did not. Shane ended his recross-examination and Carpenter was excused after a short redirect by The Colonel that established Harry had two old milk cans and two new ones.

Deputy Sheriff Leone Pickup was recalled to the stand and The Colonel resumed questioning where he had left off when Carpenter was recalled by the judge. Pickup identified the picture in evidence that showed him in a wooded setting pointing at two sticks with white flags. He stated the white flags marked the spots where Ira Bennett claimed to have found the milk cans on McGraw Road.

The Colonel changed the topic to the acquisition by Pickup of Freddy Lindsay's fingerprints when Freddy was booked at the Sheriff's Office in Little Valley. Because fingerprint technology was fairly new, The Colonel had Pickup describe the process of imprinting Freddy's fingers and thumbs using inkpads and a fingerprint card. When Pickup was done, The Colonel asked him what he had done with the card that bore Freddy's fingerprints. Pickup testified that he delivered the card to Elmer Lee, the fingerprint expert in Jamestown. Pickup produced the card in question and it was entered as evidence. The Colonel turned Leone over to Syd Shane for cross-examination.

Shane began with questions concerning the place settings in

the kitchen. He wanted to be sure that there were table settings for only two people on the kitchen table. Pickup affirmed that there were two place settings on the table when he arrived at the farmhouse.

Pickup proved to be a tough customer when Shane asked him to recall a conversation they'd had on March 25 on the topic of table settings in the Farnsworth kitchen.

"Did you not tell me, in answer to my question about two place settings...," Shane began, moving in close to Pickup's face, "did you not answer, 'I am not absolutely positive but my recollection is there were two places set at the table'?"

"Really, the only thing that I recall that we talked...."

"I did not ask you that! I asked you, did I not ask you that question and did you not make that answer!"

"I don't remember but one thing you asked me, one question."

"We had a long conversation there, did we not?"

"Not so long."

"There was a stenographer there taking down what we were saying?"

"There was."

"And we were there for thirty or forty minutes?"

"I don't believe it was that long, Mr. Shane."

"How long do you think we were there?"

"I don't believe you were there over fifteen minutes."

Shane tried to grind down Pickup on the topic of place settings but he was unsuccessful. Shane moved on to the white knit cap found near Harry's hips on the floor next to his body. Then he asked Pickup to estimate the distance between the knife and the pried-open cashbox. Pickup placed them at a distance of six inches. Shane ended his cross-examination and Pickup was excused from the stand when The Colonel declined to redirect.

Elmer A. Lee was then called to the stand to testify for the

State. The Colonel wasted no time establishing Lee as an expert in fingerprinting. Much of Lee's testimony centered on explaining that a fingerprint was the result of impressions made by the ridges of the fingers where the sweat comes out of the skin's pores. He was prompted to explain that special powders are required to develop latent fingerprints and that the basic difference in powders was color. A dark color worked better on a light surface and vice versa.

"What is your opinion as to the possibility of two persons having the same sets of fingerprints?" The Colonel asked Lee.

"There is no possible way of figuring it out that I know of."

"I show you People's Exhibit 46. Do you recognize it?"

"Yes, sir."

"What is it?"

"The fingerprints of Alfred Lindsay."

"Where did you get them?"

"From Leone Pickup."

Lee testified that he dusted the axe with special aluminum powder and found no latent prints on it. When asked about the cashboxes, Lee explained that he dusted both and found several latent prints on the smaller of the two boxes. He then testified that he took pictures of the prints with a special camera built just for taking fingerprint pictures.

Judge Larkin interrupted The Colonel and told him this was a good place to adjourn for the day. He advised everyone to report back to court the next day at ten o'clock. The courtroom emptied slowly after he retired to his chambers.

Realizing that The Colonel was nearing the end of his list of prospective witnesses, Shane thought a brief chat with Freddy would be appropriate.

"Deputy?" asked Shane. "Would you mind giving us a few minutes alone with our client? There are a few items we need to discuss with him."

"Sure," replied one of the deputies. "But we have to cuff him to you or Mr. McCarthy. Sheriff's orders. Except during the trial, Lindsay has to be cuffed at all times."

"Fine! Fine, deputy. Handcuff him to me. Just be quick about it!" Shane said impatiently as he raised his right arm.

"Freddy," Shane began. "This is it, now. It's very likely that we will be given the opportunity to open with our defense sometime tomorrow. We need your help if we are going to have a chance of beating the two capital charges you are up against. You haven't given us one thing to go on. This is your last chance to provide us with something that could help your defense. What do you say? Are you ready to do that now?"

Freddy sat and stared at the tabletop. For a few moments he said nothing. Without looking at either one of his attorneys, he eventually said, "I told you when I met you there was nothin' more I could say that would make any difference. You guys do what you want. I trust you."

"All right, have it your way. If you change your mind before we see you in the morning, you call me, or you call Mac. Okay?"

"Sure."

Shane motioned for the deputies and they came over and uncuffed him. Shane and McCarthy remained sitting at the defense table as they watched Freddy being led out of the courtroom.

"Syd?" said Mac. "What the hell are we going to do tomorrow if we have to open?"

"I don't know," Syd replied. "But hopefully, I will get an idea before we enter court tomorrow. Let's get out of here and go home, shall we?"

The traffic around the courthouse was still heavy but not jammed. Shane and McCarthy chatted briefly in the parking lot, then got into their respective cars and left for Salamanca. Shane had dinner with his wife for the first time that week. He left for his office at seven o'clock.

Shane spent several hours reading through the small mountain of notes he had made since the day he met Freddy Lindsay at the jail. He pored over them, looking for the one detail that might break The Colonel's case of two capital murder charges. After four grueling hours, Shane had to admit there was nothing in his notes he could use as an anchor for his defense strategy. He scribbled down some remarks for tomorrow's proceedings and went home. He spent a sleepless night.

The peace that settled over Little Valley that night, April 4, belied the chaos that would descend upon it when the sun rose over the hills of Cattaraugus County the next morning.

Chapter Fourteen

Every road in and out of Little Valley was filled with traffic as dawn broke on Friday, April 5. A rumor had spread overnight that Freddy might take the stand in his own defense that day. Sheriff Carlson was in his office by seven o'clock and had deputized ten former deputies to help with security and crowd control. He had men stationed in two concentric rings around the courthouse and the jail. He posted several roving deputies on the courthouse lawn, and several more at the doors to the courthouse.

Sheriff Carlson ordered Deputy Sheriff Pickup and a few other detectives to assist the sheriff's telephone operator in contacting all parties whose presence in the courtroom was mandatory for court to convene at ten o'clock. Carlson also arranged for car parking in the yard next to the jail and told the deputies, "I don't give a damn if you have to drive their cars over the courthouse lawn in order to park them yourselves. Do whatever it takes to get these essential people into the courthouse!" As a result, everyone on the mandatory list was able to get into town and park their vehicles in the yard. By nine o'clock, the streets had reached the gridlock stage. Traffic had come to a halt on Court Street.

The circus atmosphere returned as newspaper boys and vendors returned to hawk their wares to the crowd. In the midst of the hubbub, Deputy Sheriff Pickup got an idea. He and several other deputies used paper and pencils to scratch out the ridged emblem of their badges. They then wrote a number on each slip, starting at 'one' and going up incrementally until they reached the maximum number of seats available in the spectator section.

When the papers were ready, they made their way through the crowd and walked up the courthouse steps. They distributed the slips of paper randomly, telling each recipient that if he lost it he would not be admitted into the courthouse. Then Pickup sent the other deputies into the crowd to spread the news that all the courthouse seats were taken.

At 9:40 a.m., Pickup escorted Lynn Blessing and the members of the press pool to the rear of the courthouse where he had them enter using a back entrance reserved for court personnel. He waited there until Freddy Lindsay was safely escorted into the back entrance before returning to the front doors of the courthouse. At 9:50 a.m., the recipients of Pickup's paper slips were led inside in single file. Harold Williams, the jeweler from whom Bernice and Harry purchased their wedding rings, was among the lucky few to gain access to the courtroom that day. The whole process of admitting spectators went off without a hitch. Pickup followed the last spectator up the courthouse stairs.

Judge Larkin took the bench at ten o'clock and asked for a roll call of the jurors, the defendant and of all potential witnesses. Satisfied that all were present, he reconvened court for the day. Elmer Lee was recalled for the People.

The Colonel resumed his questioning of Lee regarding photographs of fingerprints he took during his investigation at the Farnsworth farmhouse on Friday, March 8. Lee explained the process of enlarging the photos to make identification of the prints easier. When he was shown the two cashboxes, Lee testified that the prints he discovered on them were still visible. He described the exact location of two fingerprints on the boxes. The Colonel produced an enlargement of the fingerprints from Freddy's middle finger of his left hand and his right thumb. Lee identified them as belonging to Freddy Lindsay and they were entered in as evidence along with the enlargements of the prints from the cashboxes.

Lee continued answering questions put to him by The

Colonel concerning the characteristics of the fingerprints. After referring to the bifurcation in a ridge of a fingerprint, he explained to the jury that a bifurcated ridge was where one ridge spread into two ridges. The bifurcation, he explained, was the point where the split began. He then showed the jury seven matching characteristics from each set of cashbox fingerprint images. The characteristics matched two of Freddy's fingerprints found on the fingerprint card he had received from Pickup. When asked, Lee explained that only four matching characteristics on a single fingerprint were required for a positive identification. He stated that without a doubt, the fingerprints on the two cashboxes belonged to Alfred Lindsay. The Colonel ended his examination of Elmer Lee.

On cross-examination, McCarthy showed that Lee had been discriminate in choosing which objects to dust for prints and which he would not dust. In testimony, Lee admitted that he completely ignored two upstairs bedrooms and the upstairs bathroom. McCarthy moved on to the prints on the cashboxes.

"Now," said McCarthy, "can you say when those prints were put on that box?"

"No, sir," said Lee.

"Is it possible that they might have been on there a week before March 8?"

"They stay on that long, sometimes. Yes, sir."

"Do they stay longer than that sometimes?"

"Yes, sir."

"Do fingerprints sometimes last two or three months on objects?"

"It all depends on how much pressure is used, how much sweat comes out of the sweat ducts of the fingers, and what surface they are on."

"So, do they sometimes last two or three months on objects?"

"They would, yes, sir."

"So, you cannot tell the day of the week or the month when those prints were placed by the defendant on People's Exhibits 31 and 32?"

"No, sir."

McCarthy pressed Lee to date the fingerprints, but the best Lee could say was that they hadn't been there "awful long."

"What do you mean by 'awful long'?" asked McCarthy.

"I imagine no longer than a week at the most," answered Lee.

"Might it have been ten days?"

"I don't think it would have been that long."

"You cannot narrow it down, can you?"

"No, I can't."

"So, is it possible that they could have been there for three weeks?"

"No, sir."

"Is it possible that they could have been there between two and three weeks?"

"They might have been. I wouldn't say for sure."

"But you do not know whether they were put there before March 5?"

"No, sir."

"That is all."

On redirect, The Colonel went over every matching characteristic from each print on the cashboxes. His questions led Lee to testify that he ignored the two bedrooms and the bathroom because he felt there was nothing in them that could be dusted for prints. Lee was excused from the stand when McCarthy declined to recross the witness. Deputy Sheriff Leone Pickup was recalled for the People.

The Colonel elicited testimony from Pickup about the milk cans, then he asked if he'd had any conversations with Freddy

Lindsay prior the time he visited the J. J. Moynihan house to investigate the murders on March 14.

"I did," answered Leone Pickup.

"And where did this conversation take place?"

"On the third floor of the jail."

"In reference to what?"

"As to the house and the articles that he left in the house."

"And what did he tell you?"

"He said he had stayed there one night."

Pickup was asked to about each article—the water jug, the lantern, and the alarm clock that had already been entered in as evidence. Pickup testified that he showed those articles to Freddy Lindsay and that Freddy identified them as the same articles he had with him in the house. The Colonel concluded his examination after Pickup testified that Freddy told him he wasn't sure if Harry Farnsworth had been wearing the white knit cap when he shot him.

Shane, on recross, went immediately to the conversation that took place between Freddy Lindsay and Leone Pickup on March 14, before Pickup went to J. J. Moynihan house.

"How did you happen to get into this conversation with Freddy?" asked Shane.

"Mr. Miller, Mr. Krieger, and I were talking together."

"Was Freddy not asked while you were there where he had stayed on Monday night?"

"I don't remember, Mr. Shane."

"And he did not state he stayed over at Nora Moynihan's across the road from her house?"

"I don't recall he said that."

"And did he not state Miss Moynihan told him he could stay there that night?"

"I remember him saying that."

"And did he not say that on Monday afternoon Miss

Moynihan gave him the keys to her brother's home across the road?"

"I don't recall him saying that."

"And did he not say that Miss Moynihan gave him a jug of water to take over and stay the night in the house?"

"Yes, he said that."

"And did he not tell you Miss Moynihan gave him blankets to take over and told him where to go in the house?"

"Yes, sir."

"And did he not tell you that Miss Moynihan gave him a clock, the clock that was sitting on the table in her front room, to take over with him to the house?"

"I believe so."

"And did he not tell you that Miss Moynihan gave him a lantern, told him where there was a lantern, out in the kitchen, and to go and get it and take it over to the Moynihan house?"

"I don't know that he put it in so many words."

"And did he not tell you, furthermore, that in order to get this stuff from Miss Moynihan's house to the J. J. Moynihan house, Nora Moynihan let him take a cart that was standing back of her shed so he could wheel the items over there?"

"He didn't say that in my presence."

Shane moved on to a different subject.

"Now, you have known Nora Moynihan a long time, have you not?"

"Yes, sir."

"And she's had a number of burglaries in her home the past few years, has she not? In her own home and in her brother's home across the way?"

"Yes, sir."

"And every time she had a burglary she called you on the telephone, did she not?"

"She has called me several times."

"Well, she has called you several times that you know of. Is that not a fact?"

"Yes, sir."

"At least three or four, is that not correct?"

"I would say two, possibly three."

"And did she say that she called you on those occasions as soon as she discovered them?"

"Yes, sir."

"Now, was there a time after March 4 when Nora Moynihan called you on the telephone and said certain things were missing from her home?"

"No, sir."

"On Friday March 8, after you had been to the Farnsworth home, after the bodies had been discovered, did you have occasion to talk to Miss Moynihan?"

"Yes, sir."

Shane went on to establish that Nora Moynihan did not call Pickup when she discovered the missing items on the morning of March 5. Pickup also testified that he did not ask Nora if she gave Freddy permission to stay at her brother's house, nor did he ask if she furnished him with the articles that were found in her brother's home on March 14. After Pickup verified that Bernice and Harold Farnsworth's bed was unmade but all the other beds in the remaining bedrooms were in an unslept condition, Shane stated he was done questioning Pickup.

During redirect, The Colonel asked if Pickup had had to break into J. J. Moynihan's house in order to gain entry. Pickup testified that he had.

On recross, Shane asked Pickup to verify that Freddy told him Nora had explained how to turn on the electricity to her brother's house by throwing a hidden switch in the cellar. Pickup was excused after The Colonel declined to redirect.

Ira Bennett was recalled to the stand and identified the milk cans as the ones he found on the side of McGraw Road.

On recross, Shane clarified Ira's answer to the previous question about the milk cans, and Ira was excused from the stand.

Ernest Tokarske was called next to testify for the People. Tokarske was the crew boss for the moving crew that emptied the Farnsworth farmhouse. He testified that Mr. Lynn Blessing instructed him to empty the house on Friday, March 15.

When Shane cross-examined Tokarske, he did not question the testimony just presented. Instead, Shane asked the witness if he knew the defendant, to which Tokarske replied he did. When it was determined that Freddy had visited Tokarske at his home on Sunday, March 3, The Colonel objected because his questioning was improper cross-examination. Judge Larkin allowed Shane to continue.

"He was at your home on Sunday?" Shane asked.

"Yes, sir," said Tokarske.

"You play in a band down there, do you not, in Steamburg?"

"Yes, sir."

"And the defendant, Freddy Lindsay, was at your home that night and took part in a discussion with regard to getting into your band?"

"Yes, sir."

"He plays a tuba, does he not, or some other instrument?"

"Yes, and the bass violin."

"Do you recall Monday, March 4?"

"Yes, sir."

"Did you see Lindsay on Monday, March 4?"

"I saw him between five and half-past five."

"And whereabouts did you see him?"

"Just across the bridge on the road going towards the Moynihans', up the hill."

"And you were riding in the opposite direction of him?"

"Yes, sir."

"And did you wave at each other?"

"Yes, sir."

"That is all," said Shane.

"That is all," said The Colonel.

Tokarske stepped down from the stand and The Colonel called Deputy Douglas A. Arrowsmith for the People.

Arrowsmith verified that the table in the kitchen had been set for two and verified the presence and the location of the knife found near the cashbox in the living room. When he verified the presence of a cap and a sweater found hanging over a dining room chair, The Colonel produced those objects. After Arrowsmith verified that they were one and the same, The Colonel entered them into evidence. Arrowsmith noted that the cap bore a label that read "A. Jacobson, North Avenue, New Rochelle." The Colonel ended his examination of Arrowsmith.

At first Shane grappled with Deputy Arrowsmith on cross-examination because the witness was reluctant to answer his questions. Eventually Arrowsmith verified the contents of the kitchen, including unfinished laundry that sat in a wash pail. After Arrowsmith verified that the Farnsworths' bed was found unmade, Shane ended his examination and The Colonel excused Arrowsmith.

Lieutenant George was recalled to the stand. The Colonel helped the lieutenant recall a conversation he'd had with Freddy on the trip back from New York City to Little Valley. He testified that Freddy Lindsay told him that he'd had gotten the best of Harry Farnsworth in a fight sometime in early February.

The Colonel spent a good deal of time refining George's earlier testimony. He ended his examination after the lieutenant testified that Freddy was aware that Harry almost always wore a knitted cap.

Shane attempted to show the jury that a lot of Lieutenant George's testimony to the court came as a result of his memory being 'refreshed' by the District Attorney prior to his initial examination on the stand. The lieutenant contradicted himself several times and Shane abandoned the effort after getting him to admit that he had done something to refresh his memory.

When The Colonel went on redirect he asked two questions. "What else did you do?"

"Just reviewed the defendant's statement," Lieutenant George replied.

"With whom?"

"The District Attorney."

After a short recross and a short redirect, Lieutenant George was excused.

Dr. Marshall Hillsman was recalled to the stand for the People. The Colonel spent an inordinate amount of time trying to get the doctor to establish that the dark stains surrounding Bernice's body were blood. The process became so lengthy that Shane finally objected. Judge Larkin settled the matter with one quick question for the doctor.

"What do you say the dark stain is?" Larkin asked.

"I am satisfied that it was blood," replied Hillsman.

Embarrassed, The Colonel took up a new line of questioning about how the severed carotid artery might spurt when it was cut without obtaining the desired response. After that he attempted to get the doctor to ascertain the position of Harry's body when he had been shot in the brain with the fatal bullet. Hillsman was only allowed to describe the angle of the gun in relation to the head when the gun was fired.

When The Colonel asked Hillsman to describe the width of the separation of bone in Bernice's skull fracture, Shane became incensed. "I object, Your Honor! The width of separation? He already described it in detail. The only purpose of this is to inflame the jury. That is the only possible reason for recalling this doctor!"

Judge Larkin sustained Shane's objection and The Colonel tried a different approach to describe the separation in the skull. Shane was having none of it and The Colonel gave up questioning the witness after the judge again sustained Shane's objection to his line of questioning. Shane declined to recross the doctor.

The Colonel faced the bench and said, "The People Rest."

Before Judge Larkin could say a word, Shane recalled Deputy Sheriff Leone Pickup to the stand. After some confusion, Judge Larkin reopened for the People because Shane wanted to cross-examine Pickup as a witness for the State and not for the Defense.

Mac McCarthy cross-examined Pickup about the presence of five holes in the eastern-facing window of the Farnsworth kitchen. When Pickup repeatedly refused to guess the size of the holes, McCarthy ended the cross-examination.

Under redirect from The Colonel, it was clearly established that the holes in the glass were not present at the time of the discovery of the bodies. When The Colonel was done with his redirect of Pickup, Judge Larkin recessed the court for lunch until two o'clock.

Court reconvened for the afternoon session promptly at two o'clock and Sheriff Lester Carlson was recalled for the People. The Sheriff testified that the Farnsworth house was under guard until the evening of March 11, and he further testified that the holes in question were not present on Friday, March 8.

The People rested their case for the second time that day after Syd Shane declined to recross the Sheriff. Shane took the opportunity to make a motion for the dismissal of Felony Murder During the Commission of Crime, but was denied. He was also denied when he made an additional motion for the dismissal of the count for Murder in the First Degree.

Shane twisted his body around and stared directly at Freddy Lindsay. He arched his eyebrows as if to say, 'Well, this is your last chance. What do you want to do?' Freddy shook his head in the negative and Shane turned back to face the judge.

Syd Shane squared his shoulders, elevated his head slightly and said, "The defendant rests, Your Honor."

"Evidence closed?" asked Judge Larkin, clearly surprised.

"Yes, Your Honor."

"Your motions are renewed, are they? Same disposition. Same exception?"

"Exception, Your Honor."

Judge Larkin turned to the jury and addressed them. "All right. You have the case."

The trial phase of the case came to a quiet end.

CHAPTER FIFTEEN

THE SPECTATORS SITTING IN THE AUDIENCE SECTION OF THE courtroom were dazed by the speed with which the Defense had closed the case. While Judge Larkin, Colonel Krieger, Syd Shane and Mac McCarthy prepared for the summation by the State and the Defense, the spectators chatted excitedly among themselves. In a short while, however, thanks to Sheriff Carlson who sat in the audience section along with them, they understood the portent of what had just occurred. They waited with great anticipation for The Colonel and Syd Shane to deliver their closing arguments.

Judge Larkin looked up from his paperwork at the bench and addressed the principal parties. "Are you gentlemen ready to proceed with summation?"

"The State is ready to sum up, Your Honor," replied The Colonel.

"Yes, Your Honor, the defense is ready for summation," Shane declared.

"All right then. Mr. Shane, you may begin for the defendant."

"Thank you, Your Honor," Shane said as he walked around the defense table and approached the jury box.

Turning to the judge and then back to the jury, Shane began his summation, his right hand holding a copy of Freddy's Grand Jury Indictment at his side. He waved his left hand with sweeping grace as he began to speak.

"May it please the Court, Gentlemen of the Jury, on Monday morning, five days ago, we commenced the trial of the case of the People of the State of New York against Alfred J. Lindsay. I know that you fully realize the seriousness of this matter that has been before us. I know everybody taking part in this trial realizes the seriousness of this matter. We have on trial a boy of whom the State is asking that he forfeit his life. I know that I, as well as you, perhaps, will feel relieved when our task is done. To me, it has been a great burden. These past five days have worn heavily on me. They have taken from my strength and, perhaps have taken greatly from what little ability I may have to properly present to you this defendant's case. I pray to God that I may have strength enough, reason and logic enough, to present this case to you, on his behalf, as he would do if he could and if he were standing here in my shoes."

The courtroom was mesmerized by the modulation and the cadence of Shane's voice as he delivered his carefully crafted dissertation. He spoke as if he were personally addressing each individual in the courtroom. Judge Larkin sat with his hands folded on the bench and his head slightly cocked towards the jury box as he listened intently to what Shane had to say.

Shane assured the jury that they had been carefully selected for their ability to reach a fair judgment for the defendant based purely on the testimony that was presented to them. Then he explained the charges for the premeditated murder of Bernice G. Farnsworth as he showed them the indictment in his hand.

"This is the first count in the indictment which the People of the State of New York charge this defendant, Alfred J. Lindsay. Realize, gentlemen, what that means. The State of New York, with its tens of millions of people, with its billions of dollars in wealth, against Alfred Lindsay! He has got but two friends and they are in this courtroom. Just two friends, and they happen to be Mr. McCarthy and myself."

Shane pleaded with the jury to expect proof from the State instead of settling for a flimsy case that might leave them to guess instead of judging Freddy fairly. Then he moved on to the second indictment for Murder During the Commission of a Felony. Again, he pleaded with them to listen to the evidence that had been presented to them and make their judgment from only that evidence.

When Shane ended his plea for justice, he summarized the testimony of each witness beginning with Ira Bennett. The worth of Ira's testimony, in his opinion, was reduced to three points. Ira could place the bodies where they were found. He could place the belongings found in the house, and he found two milk cans about five hundred feet from the house.

In summing up William Whitmore's testimony, Shane pointed out that Whitmore served only to reiterate Ira's testimony with the exception of his testimony concerning the character of Harold Farnsworth. "Whitmore testified that he knew Farnsworth, that he had worked on the Farnsworth farm as a hired hand, that Farnsworth was a man of nasty disposition, of mean temper, that he would club his horses, that he would put the club to them when they would not move. Now, that is of some importance in this case as bearing on what type of fellow Mr. Farnsworth was."

The testimony of Clifford Cheney, Superintendent of Public Works for the City of Salamanca, and the map he produced for the People were portrayed by Shane as accurate. He said he had no criticism of Cheney's testimony.

Photographer Sylvester Nodler's testimony was also portrayed as accurate, but Shane pointed out an omission that disturbed him. "Of all of the photographs that are marked in evidence—the photos taken at the Farnsworth home—of all the rooms in the Farnsworth house of which pictures were taken, you cannot find in those exhibits one picture of the kitchen and its appointments, particularly as to the kitchen table and what was on it. Why, why, have the People failed to produce before you a photograph of the kitchen to show you what its condition was on March 8? Is there some reason for it? If there is, will the District

Attorney explain it to the jury, to their satisfaction? Are you not entitled as jurors to all the facts in this case? Not just to a part of them, before you form your opinion on the defendant's guilt or innocence? Are not the People of the State of New York required to do so, before they can ask for a verdict sending this boy to the electric chair? Are they not required to give you all of the facts in their possession?"

Moving on, Shane explained to the jury that he and Mac McCarthy's hands had been tied from the start, when they were denied access to the crime scene as it was when Ira Bennett first walked into it on March 8. Again, he assailed the District Attorney for his failure to produce a kitchen photograph and suggested that The Colonel was withholding crucial evidence.

Fred Houlihan's testimony was boiled down to one key fact—that he placed Freddy in the garage on Tuesday, March 5 fifth and not on the correct date, Monday, March 4.

Regarding the testimony given by Jay Stevens, Shane placed emphasis on the fact that he, too, gave the wrong day, Tuesday, as the day Freddy sat in Houlihan's Garage in Steamburg.

When Shane spoke about the testimony given by Robert Deppa, he launched into a strong argument about the discrepancy between the testimonies of Deppa and Nora Moynihan. Moynihan's testimony clearly placed Freddy at her home and the garage in Steamburg on Monday, March 4. Deppa, among others, placed Freddy there on Tuesday. Shane used Nora Moynihan's testimony as a fulcrum to support his argument concerning the correct date.

"Now, is there any man on this jury, any single man on this jury, who believes that Freddy Lindsay and Mr. and Mrs. Farnsworth were in Steamburg on Tuesday afternoon, March 5? That is the evidence offered by the People. That is the evidence that they want you to believe!"

Shane bolstered his argument about Fred Houlihan's

testimony regarding Harry's purchase at the Jacquay store in Steamburg.

"...that Farnsworth could not pay for the meat and for that reason he wanted Houlihan to go with him to Jacquay's, to go his credit, to go good for him. The reason that Farnsworth could not pay for the meat was because he did not get his milk check. His milk check was not due until the fifth day of March, which was Tuesday."

Shane also pointed out holes in the Houlihan, Deppa and Jay Stevens testimonies about Freddy's presence at the Steamburg garage on March 5. Shane ended his clarification succinctly. "You have got your choice. You cannot take both. You cannot believe Miss Moynihan and at the same time believe these others. Their stories do not mix. They are diametrically opposed. So much for Mr. Houlihan, Jay Stevens, Leon Johnson and Robert Deppa."

The testimony of John Monroe, a farmer from Coldspring, was discounted by Shane in the same manner as the testimony given by the other men who had been present at Houlihan's Garage in Steamburg.

Shane used Dr. Hillsman's testimony about the autopsies he performed on Bernice and Harry Farnsworth to place doubt on Coroner Middleton's testimony concerning a powder burn he said was found on Harry's left forearm. Hillsman testified that he did not observe the powder burn in question.

"I do not say that anyone is deliberately telling any lie about that. I know Mr. Middleton. I know Dr. Hillsman. They are both high-class men and neither of them would deliberately come into this courtroom and lie about that subject. But someone here is mistaken. Either Dr. Hillsman is mistaken or Mr. Middleton."

Then, Shane summed up Nora Moynihan's testimony. He led the jury through her testimony, point by point. He used her testimony to chronicle the movements of Freddy Lindsay and the Farnsworths on Monday, March 4. He cast doubt on her testimony regarding the articles she said came up missing the day after Freddy was at her home. Shane suggested to the jury that Nora Moynihan's motive for lying to Deputy Sheriff Leone Pickup about the burglary was to cover up the fact that she had given those articles to Freddy and provided him with permission to sleep in her brother's house.

"My only answer to that is that Miss Moynihan possibly thought she might be implicated if she were to admit giving Lindsay the use of her brother's home and the use of these articles that came from her home. Either that, or her brother, who owned the home, might criticize her for permitting somebody to go over to his home and stay all night. I am satisfied that nobody believes this boy actually stole these articles from Nora Moynihan and I am satisfied that this jury believes she did give him the use of those things."

When Shane concluded his remarks concerning Moynihan's testimony about the missing items, Judge Larkin spoke up. "Mr. Shane, I am going to interrupt you so that you may guide your summation accordingly. I have made up my mind that I will submit on the common law felony theory and no felony theory."

It appeared as if the judge had dismissed the charge of Murder During the Commission of a Felony count. The Colonel was worried because Syd Shane was proving he was, indeed, a formidable litigator already producing results midway into his summation.

Shane thanked the judge and continued his summation. Regarding the testimonies of Patrolman Walsh, Detective Clancy, and Inspector McDermott, Shane told the jury that it was McDermott who had impressed him most.

"McDermott took the witness stand and he told you what occurred in New York City when they found the defendant, Alfred Lindsay. He repeated to you the story that Lindsay told him about the murders in Coldspring. He said that when Lindsay was brought into the police station he had said, 'I am glad I am here. I want to talk. I want to tell you about this occurrence at Coldspring.' And Freddy Lindsay proceeded to do it."

Shane went through McDermott's testimony point-by-point and used it as a vehicle to provide Freddy's version of the events that occurred at the Farnsworth farm on that fateful day, March 4. He paid particular attention to Freddy's claim that he had been struck by Harry Farnsworth first. Then Shane drove home the fact that Freddy stated very clearly that it was Harry Farnsworth, not he, who had picked up the axe and brandished it against Freddy in the cellar.

"In the scuffle, Farnsworth got hold of an axe, took it in his hand and said to Lindsay, 'I have a notion to split your head open.' Bear in mind that Farnsworth was a man of one hundred and seventy pounds, five-feet-seven, rugged, robust in build. Here was Lindsay, unarmed, facing a man larger in size, a man whom he had known to be quarrelsome, with an axe in his hand. And, they had been quarreling! He did the same thing you or I would have done under the same circumstances, I am sure. Lindsay grabbed the axe, struggled with Farnsworth, took the axe away from Farnsworth and then he swung. He swung it at Farnsworth. And when he did, Mrs. Farnsworth jumped in between them and the axe struck her. Then everything swam before his eyes. Lindsay kept swinging the axe. He does not know how many times he swung it. He swung it. The result was that Mrs. Farnsworth was killed. She met a horrible, horrible death. She was killed, however, in an accident, not through any premeditation on the part of this boy.

"What is the theory on which the District Attorney hopes to base here a conviction of Murder in the First Degree? He must prove to you and the Court that, beyond a reasonable doubt, Mrs. Farnsworth was killed by a premeditated act on the part of Lindsay."

As he continued, Shane implored the jury to find a motive for Freddy's premeditation and he assured them that they would find no motive for that in the testimony that had been presented to them. He stated that the testimony given regarding the Farnsworths' banking transactions proved that there could not have been more than seven dollars in cash in their home on Monday, March 4. Once again, he exhorted the jury to prove a motive for the charge of premeditated murder.

"Are you going to guess at why this thing occurred or are you going to decide it on the evidence? Who knows what occurred in the cellar of the Farnsworth home? Only one person on this earth, only one person on the face of this earth knows! That is Alfred Lindsay. He has told his story to the Inspector of Police at New York, to the District Attorney who has his signed and full statement of what occurred. He told his story to this Inspector of the Police and it is almost identical to the story that he told to Colonel Krieger, the District Attorney, under four hours of cross-examination and grilling by him, the Lieutenant of the State Police, the Sheriff of this county and the special investigator of the District Attorney. And there, on the District Attorney's desk, lies a stenographic record of the questions that Lindsay was asked and the answers he gave, consisting of eighty typewritten pages consolidated into five-and-one-half pages dictated by the District Attorney and signed by the defendant."

As Shane was stating that the District Attorney had not submitted the stenographic record of Lindsay's interrogation, he walked to the jury box and gripped the railing in front of it with both hands.

"Now, when District Attorney Krieger, in summing up this case, said to you, 'It is true, I do have the stenographic record of this conversation and Mr. Shane could have had it and put it into evidence,' but that record is not my property. It is the property of the District Attorney. It is not my duty to prove Lindsay guilty of this crime. The burden is on his shoulders, not on mine."

Satisfied with his discussion of the previous witnesses, Shane addressed the testimony given by Sheriff Lester Carlson. Shane castigated the sheriff for his failure to take the suitcase in the kitchen into evidence, and he questioned why Carlson had not mentioned the suitcase to the jury. He suggested that the suitcase may have aided Freddy in some way. He asked the jury to question the sheriff's motive for not taking the suitcase into custody as possible evidence. When Shane finished with Carlson's testimony, he wrapped up his summation.

"We ask you not to permit any sympathy to enter into your verdict and we do not want any prejudice or passion to enter into your verdict either. We want a verdict on the evidence. We want you to comb the evidence with a fine-toothed comb and then say, 'How did the death of Mrs. Farnsworth occur and why did it occur?' Answer both those questions. Answer them so that your conscience is clear, so that when you have rendered your verdict you can go home and you can sleep. So that you will not have to, for the rest of your days, carry around in your mind the thought that you have sent a man to the electric chair for the premeditated murder of Bernice Farnsworth. You are the one that has to carry the load, not me. That is your burden.

"Remember, gentlemen, in your deliberations, that you are dealing with three of the most important things in the world. You are dealing with life. You are dealing with death. And you are dealing with eternity! You are the judges. Move carefully. Deliberate. Take your time. Sift this evidence. Be sure."

In a courtroom that was completely silent, Syd Shane gave the jury a sweeping gaze, turned, and walked away from them. Several of the spectators began to clap but stopped abruptly as they realized this was not a theatrical performance. The spectators had certainly gotten what they had hoped for from Shane's oration. His eloquent and emotional summation would remain in their memories for a very long time.

Judge Larkin recessed the court in order to give the jury a well-deserved break. He told them that the District Attorney would present his summation upon their return to the courtroom.

Freddy Lindsay sat and chatted with Shane and McCarthy while they waited for the jury to return. The Colonel sat at the prosecutor's table writing furiously. He made some hasty changes to his summation notes as a result of Shane's summation and the judge's ruling on the felony count. He was fully prepared to sum up the People's case against Alfred J. Lindsay when the jury was ushered back into the courtroom.

Colonel Krieger paused for a few moments after Judge Larkin reconvened the court. He then rose from his seat and slowly walked across the courtroom towards the jury.

The Colonel spoke directly to the jurors. "May it please the Court and Gentlemen of the jury, I have now the most difficult duty that devolves upon one so unfortunate as to occupy the position which I now hold. I have now the duty of asking you to convict a man of the most serious crime known to our law, that of murder in the first degree.

"In a short time, the Court will submit to you the question that you were sworn to try here truly on the evidence, the guilt or the lack of it, of Alfred J. Lindsay, for this crime with which he is charged. We have been hedging around here a little bit. We have been very careful. Nobody wants to prejudice a jury against any defendant. I hope every defendant ever tried in this courtroom has as fair a trial as Alfred. J. Lindsay has had.

"The Court will soon submit to you the question you were sworn to try truly here on the evidence, the guilt or the lack of it, of Alfred J. Lindsay for the crime with which he is charged."

The Colonel commended defense counsel Syd Shane and Mac McCarthy for having done their duty well in defense of Freddy Lindsay. He told the jury that their task would be, indeed, the hardest to complete. He assured them he was confident they would reach their decision based upon the evidence and that the evidence would convince them beyond a reasonable doubt that Freddy Lindsay was guilty as charged.

The Colonel agreed with Shane. "Yes, Freddy Lindsay has had a fair trial. He has not had the kind of trial that Bernice Farnsworth had. She had no attorneys assigned to her by the Court. She had nobody to speak to in her defense. She was not even protected to the extent of an indictment against her for anything this defendant may have fancied she did. She was cut down in cold blood by a ruthless beast! Cut down like you would cut a limb off a tree!

"The defense counsel referred to Lindsay as 'this boy.' Boy? Alfred Lindsay is twenty-nine years old! Look at those shoulders! Look at that development! You can see it through his clothes. 'This boy' who found it necessary to chop down that little woman, four-feet-eleven inches tall, with an axe! Not once, cold and deliberate as he was. One blow was not enough. He had to turn to practically chop her head off! He asks you for sympathy?"

Shane became concerned as he watched several jurors shake their heads in agreement with The Colonel's statements. The Colonel then explained the requirements for a verdict based on reasonable doubt. He pressed the jurors to come to the obvious conclusion and convict the defendant of murder in the first degree.

The Colonel advised them that the Court would give them the option of convicting Freddy Lindsay of murder in a lesser degree. "Again I pray you, pay close attention to the Court's Charge. Do not mistake what he tells you. Do not say, 'Well, we hate to take a man's life. Isn't there something else we can convict him of?' That is not what you are sworn to do, gentleman. You are sworn to decide this case on evidence and that is all I, and that is all anyone, can ask of you. You do not have anything to do with punishment. You and I did not make the laws of this State. We are here enforcing them. I am here presenting the People's version of this case. I am here telling you what inferences you should draw. You are here to weigh my claims and those of opposing counsel."

When speaking of a motive for the murder, The Colonel made light of its importance. He told the jury that no motive could ever explain the dastardly deed that Freddy Lindsay committed on the fifth of March. He appealed to the jury's emotions concerning the ramifications of the death of Bernice and Harold Farnsworth at Freddy Lindsay's hand.

"We cannot resurrect Bernice Farnsworth or her husband and have them tell us about the grievances and the difficulties that had occurred in their household. They cannot tell us their story. The defendant has told us his and he, an interested witness, asks you to believe his story. But the other principals in this tragedy have not been permitted to tell theirs, gentlemen."

At that point, The Colonel returned to the issue of motive. "What was the motive? Was it revenge because the poor innocent victims of his rage did not want him around there? Was it because of the quarrels they'd had? Was it because of some grievance against Farnsworth because of the fight they had in February? Was it due to something that neither you nor I know about? When Lindsay was sitting around Houlihan's Garage, around Miss Moynihan's house, around the corners there at Steamburg with his head in his hands as he is doing right now, gentlemen, what do you suppose was going through his mind then? What was he thinking about? What was he planning? He has not told you that in his statement, gentlemen. Was the motive robbery? Was the motive to get money? I do not know."

The Colonel raised the topic of Bernice Farnsworth's bank withdrawal and the deposit of the cash from that withdrawal into the State Bank of Randolph. He brought up doubt that Freddy knew the money had been deposited in another bank. He proposed that Lindsay might have thought the cash was stored in the

Farnsworths' cashbox. He said the discovery of Freddy Lindsay's fingerprints on the cashbox proved beyond a reasonable doubt that he had pried it open.

The Colonel finally broached the subject of the date Freddy Lindsay and the Farnsworths visited Steamburg. "I do not know whether this couple was in Steamburg on Monday or Tuesday afternoon. I do not think that it makes a whole lot of difference. That does not tell us what happened on Tuesday, sometime in the morning or the afternoon. Harold and Bernice Farnsworth were foully murdered in their home, the home they hoped to make a pleasant home, the home in which they had taken in this ingrate and given him a place to live, put him up in a bedroom in their own dwelling, treated him like one of the family."

The Colonel's next topic was Doctor Hillsman's testimony, for which he extolled the doctor's medical prowess. "He has told you that, in his opinion, the blow on Mrs. Farnsworth's skull, on the right side of her face, this blow which split the skull, broke that bone entirely in two, all the way to the back part of the head. This same blow split her skull in the other direction, broke her nose. This blow that laid her forehead open was inflicted while she stood up. Dr. Hillsman testified that this blow, which split her head open like a pumpkin, could have been inflicted with a weapon like the axe found beside her!"

The Colonel then demonstrated that Freddy's account of the murders was flawed. "During the altercation that killed her, this woman came from Lindsay's right, in between them, as if you were standing in Lindsay's place and I was Mrs. Farnsworth, walking between you and the stenographer here, and as he swung that axe, Lindsay suddenly saw her face loom before him. How did she get the blow on the right side of her face? Did she not have to get it on the left? Dr. Hillsman told you that, in his opinion, the wicked blow came from the direction of her right front, and that the bursting of the skull that followed gave the burst in the direction from which the impact came. The defendant says Mrs. Farnsworth rolled around the cellar. He says he saw her bleeding. But not one drop of blood was on her face. Not one other vestige of her blood was in that whole place except where it gushed out of her carotid artery. This fellow cut her head off, completely severed the carotid artery, the jugular vein, the trachea, the spine itself, the most brutish, fiendish thing imaginable! That little woman did not weigh one hundred and ten pounds. Accident? Self defense?"

The Colonel moved on to addressing Sylvester Nodler's crime scene photographs. He assured the jury that nothing had been moved as the Defense might have them believe. The chair identified as missing in the photo was not visible due to the angle at which the photos had been taken. The angle was necessary because of limitations caused by walls and other obstructions.

Addressing the absence of kitchen photos, The Colonel said, "No, gentlemen, we do not have any picture of the kitchen. I am sorry. I wish we had time to take a picture of every room in the house for you. But we could not keep the bodies there overnight. We had to let the fingerprint man get to work. We had to take some of those things away to preserve them as exhibits, and, gentlemen, as a result, we have no pictures of the kitchen. You must depend upon the memory of witnesses and try to find the truth from their testimony."

The Colonel's summation stretched on and he was losing the interest of some of the jurors. Undaunted by their obvious inattention, he attempted to shoot holes in Freddy's statement. He discounted Freddy's claim that he grabbed the axe from Harry Farnsworth and swung it to keep the larger man away from him. Again he reminded the jury that Freddy was the only witness and that he was a prejudiced one. He reminded the jury that Lindsay had been integral in the compilation of his statement. He reminded them about the changes Freddy made to the document before affixing his signature on each of the six typewritten pages.

Finally, The Colonel gave a version of what he thought had really occurred at the Farnsworth farm on the day of the murders. He attempted to inflame the emotions of the juror at every turn by playing up the brutality of the crime and the defenselessness of his victims. When he spoke of Harry Farnsworth's murder, The Colonel discounted Freddy's story about lying in wait, Bernice's gun in his hand, for Harry to come back downstairs.

"He could have lain in wait for Mr. Farnsworth in the alcove of the stairs and he could have shot Farnsworth in cold blood. Cold blood? How cold? So cold that when he knocked him down with that first bullet, he could have stood above him and sent another bullet through Farnsworth's brain. That second bullet is the fatal one, the bullet that killed Farnsworth. But then he points the gun down at the prone figure and shoots, point-blank at Mr. Farnsworth's eye, so close that he burns the skin and singes the eyebrow, to make sure of his job. The defense wants you to say, gentlemen, that the killing of Bernice Farnsworth was not done with premeditation and deliberation."

It was obvious that The Colonel was ready to wrap up his summation and the courtroom stirred in anticipation of an impassioned closing.

"But now, just think again, of the scene in that cellar. Why, he could have killed Mrs. Farnsworth with his fist! He did not need an axe. He could have killed her with his bare, naked hands! With one hand he could have snuffed out that frail little life!

"Gentlemen, I think that you are fully convinced that this is the most fiendish, brutal, cowardly crime that you or I ever heard of, and no jury in Cattaraugus County, gentlemen, not any jury anywhere in this land of ours, could possibly, after hearing this evidence, do aught but return the only possible verdict in this case, that of guilty of the crime in the murder of the first degree. I thank you very much for your patient attention."

As it had been when Syd Shane finished his summation, the courtroom remained absolutely silent as The Colonel walked back to his table. He was scowling at Freddy, who sat hunched over. The Colonel's summation had been powerful and he had sparked an angry flame in the jury.

Before delivering his instructions to the jury, Judge Larkin ordered the County Clerk, Guy Fargo, to read the statement that Freddy gave to the District Attorney on March 14 to the jury in its entirety. When Fargo finished reading the statement it was entered in as evidence. Judge Larkin called for another recess and reminded the jury that they were not to begin deliberations until they received the Charge of the Court.

Court reconvened at half past four and Judge Larkin began his instructions to the jury. All sound in the Courtroom hushed as he spoke. "We have reached the conclusion of a very important trial. The part played in it by the Counsel, the District Attorney representing the People of this State and the two attorneys representing the defendant, their part has been important. The part I have had in it has also been important. But that which you are now called upon to do is perhaps the most important part in the whole trial. After all, the responsibility is yours."

The judge reminded each juror that they had taken a solemn oath to decide Alfred Lindsay's case solely upon evidence and nothing else. He carefully explained the charges against Lindsay and told them that he had dropped the second count of the indictment because he believed no evidence supported that charge.

The judge patiently defined the term "reasonable doubt" for them. Then he defined the charge of Murder in the First Degree. He explained that the jury could find the defendant guilty of murder in a lesser degree than what the indictment indicated. He defined those lesser degrees as murder in the second degree, manslaughter and manslaughter in the second degree.

Judge Larkin then explained the terms "deliberation" and

"premeditation." He instructed them to look for those two things among the evidence given regarding the commission of the crime. He reminded them that Alfred Lindsay was not on trial for Harry Farnsworth's murder and that testimony had been allowed about it for the purposes of throwing light on the murder of Bernice Farnsworth.

In logical progression, Judge Larkin reviewed some of the testimony that had been presented. He chronicled the discovery of the bodies through the testimonies of Ira Bennett and William Whitmore, and about the condition of the body in Dr. Hillsman's testimony. He re-read the portion of Freddy's statement regarding his movements from the time he woke up in the morning on March 5, to the time he left the Farnsworth farm in Bernice's Sport Coupe. He pointed out that the defendant had freely admitted in his statement that he struck the blows that killed Bernice Farnsworth.

A few jurors were visibly surprised when Judge Larkin informed them that it was their option to believe or disbelieve the content of Freddy Lindsay's statement, as much of it could not be corroborated by evidence. He also told them that if they believed Bernice ran in between the two men as Lindsay was trying to repel her husband's attack and that she was killed by accident, then they should discharge the indictment against him and let Alfred Lindsay go free.

"If you do not believe his statement that he was repelling an attack by Harry Farnsworth, and if you reach the conclusion that he struck Mrs. Farnsworth with the axe, and based on testimony regarding the character of the wounds, then you may find the defendant guilty of murder in the first degree beyond a reasonable doubt."

Judge Larkin addressed Freddy's flight to New York City and said it indicated that Mr. Lindsay wished to conceal himself. "Flight is not conclusive, but it is a circumstance that a jury may consider as evidencing a consciousness of guilt on the part of the one fleeing."

The judge returned to the topic of deliberation and premeditation and instructed the jurors that they may consider the repetition of the blows delivered during the murder of Mrs. Farnsworth when determining Mr. Lindsay's guilt.

Judge Larkin's next topic was the concern Syd Shane raised regarding Freddy's lack of motive. He told the jurors to consider the looting of bedrooms and the prying open of the cashbox as evidence of motive. He also said that establishing a motive was not essential in determining guilt for a crime.

As Judge Larkin neared the end of his jury instructions, he said there were only two possible verdicts in this case, not guilty or guilty of one of the four possible charges he had outlined earlier in his instructions.

In closing his instructions to the jury, the judge said, "As I said earlier, this case is important to the defendant, and to the People of the State, the People of this County. They have a right to expect that jurors will perform their duties conscientiously, that they will examine a defense with care, that they will accord to a defendant every right to which he is entitled under the law. And at the same time, they will be equally just to organized society as a whole. If guilt is established, the jury will say so by their verdict."

The Colonel and Syd Shane requested further instructions to the jurors on points including compelling the jurors to return to the Court if there is any unresolved discrepancy in testimony, and reminding the jury that the defendant had no burden of proof to sustain that he acted in self-defense. When the pleas of the State and the Defense were exhausted, Judge Larkin made an official ruling on the felony count.

"And I will now, at this time, grant your motion dismissing the second count of the indictment. It has been dismissed, but not formally dismissed, leaving nothing but the first count of the indictment."

Syd Shane stood and addressed the Court. "If Your Honor please, how about the thirteenth juror?"

"Oh!" exclaimed the judge, "The thirteenth juror, of course, was discharged at the conclusion of the case. You will not participate in the deliberations at all, Mr. Juror."

Charles Eberts, the thirteenth juror, stepped down from the juror box and joined the spectators in the audience section of the courtroom.

At 5:37 in the evening, Judge Larkin turned to the jury and said, "All right. You may retire, gentlemen. I suggest that you order their supper, deputy."

With the exception of Lynn Blessing and the newspaper reporters, no one left the courtroom. They wanted to savor the experience for just a bit longer. The Colonel straightened his papers and placed them in a neat stack. He avoided making eye contact with Syd Shane or Mac McCarthy. Eventually, the bailiff began shooing the spectators out of the courtroom and closed the doors behind the last one.

Freddy Lindsay was led from the courtroom and taken to the jail for supper. He would remain in his cell until the jury came back with its verdict. Shane and McCarthy ordered supper delivered to the courtroom and sat at the defense table waiting for it to arrive. The Colonel retired to his office and ate his supper there. All three attorneys remained at the courthouse because they expected a verdict to be returned in a matter of hours.

The time moved slowly as Shane and McCarthy picked over their dinners, and finally they just pushed them aside. Shane's stomach was in knots. He was under the extreme pressure of being responsible for the life of another person. He second-guessed everything he had said and done before and during the trial. In the end he still could not predict the outcome.

Shane and McCarthy sat alone in the courtroom until eight o'clock, when The Colonel returned and sat down at the Prosecutor's table. Shane and McCarthy decided to go out for a smoke and returned at 8:45. They sat in silence until 9:37 p.m., when the bailiff rushed into the courtroom and informed the men that the jury had reached a verdict.

By ten o'clock, the judge, the jury, a small group of spectators, and Freddy Lindsay sat in the courtroom waiting for Acting Court Clerk, Rollin Pratt, to arrive. When Pratt entered, he called the roll and all were present in the courtroom.

Clerk Pratt turned to the jury foreman, Eber Russell of New Albion, and said, "Gentlemen, have you agreed upon your verdict?"

"We have," responded Russell.

"How do you find?"

"Your honor, if the Court please, we have arrived at a verdict of Guilty of Murder in the First Degree."

Syd Shane felt as though he had been struck in the head. He swooned for a moment, then worked to regain his composure. From somewhere far away he heard himself say to Judge Larkin, "Your Honor, if the Court please, may the clerk poll the jury?"

Pratt polled the jury and they all affirmed their vote for the guilty verdict. Judge Larkin thanked the jury and formally discharged them from their service to the State.

"If Your Honor, please," Shane said to the judge, "at this time I move for a new trial under Section Four-sixty-five of the Code of Criminal Procedure and on all the grounds stated here and particularly upon the ground that the verdict is against the weight of evidence."

"That is denied," ruled Judge Larkin. "This Court is about to adjourn. But for that fact, the defendant would be entitled to two days for the imposition of the sentence. Is that waived?"

"We will waive that," Shane said mechanically.

"And the sentence may be pronounced at once?"

"Yes."

"All right. Bring the defendant forward."

Freddy was cuffed and led to the bench by deputies who held his each of his arms tightly in their grasp. Freddy stood before the judge with his head cast down in shame. Judge Larkin pronounced sentence on him. "Alfred J. Lindsay, you have been convicted after what I consider a fair trial. You have been defended by competent counsel. We have endeavored in every way to protect your rights and the jury has returned a verdict that is fully in accord with the facts as proved. The sentence is mandatory in your case. The sentence of the Court is that the Sheriff of Cattaraugus County deliver you to the Warden and the Agent of Sing Sing Correctional Facility and there you shall be put to death according to the law commencing May 13, 1935."

Sheriff Carlson approached the bench and addressed his deputies, "Get him the hell out of here! I want this man in a car and on his way to Sing Sing within the hour!"

The sheriff's deputies dragged Freddy out of the courtroom through the rear door. Within forty-five minutes, two cars left the jailhouse yard. Freddy Lindsay was in car number one with Sheriff Carlson and Deputy Sheriff Pickup. Car number two contained three deputies who kept watch over the sheriff's car from the rear in case Freddy attempted an escape. A small crowd of people watched as the cars motored by and disappeared from view.

The crowd was small by the time the verdict had come in from the jury. The cold temperature of the April evening had driven most of the spectators away from the courthouse lawn. Only those fortunate enough to find space in the warm courthouse lobby remained when the guilty verdict was delivered upstairs. The courtroom spectators left slowly, like exhausted guests leaving a long, spirited party. By 11:30 p.m., Little Valley was fully transformed back into the sleepy, rural seat of Cattaraugus County. The process of forgetting all about Bernice and Harold Farnsworth, and their murderer, Freddy Lindsay, had begun.

CHAPTER SIXTEEN

SHERIFF CARLSON'S CAR BOUNCED VIOLENTLY WHEN IT encountered a sizeable pothole on Rock City Road shortly after it drove away from the jailhouse in Little Valley. Deputy Sheriff Leone Pickup and Freddy Lindsay, who were handcuffed to one another, were thrown violently around in the back seat of the car. Freddy cried softly as the other occupants of the car settled back into their seats. Pickup was surprised to find he actually felt sorry for Freddy.

Sheriff Lester Carlson wasn't as sympathetic as Pickup. He was still stinging from the unflattering gossip that had circulated through the county regarding his decision to beef up security around the courthouse and jail during the trial, for allowing Lynn Blessing to clear the Farnsworth farmhouse prematurely, and for not taking the infamous suitcase into custody as potential evidence. He saw Freddy as the root of his current problems and he wanted the man out of his custody as soon as possible.

Carlson drove into Salamanca and turned onto Route 17. He was retracing a portion of the escape route Freddy had taken a month earlier on his way to New York City. After half an hour, Freddy stopped crying and within minutes had completely regained his composure. Pickup was surprised by the transition. Freddy became talkative and animated. The finality of the death sentence seemed to have lost its impact on him. He accepted his pending death and decided to make the best of his last few hours in the free world.

Bored and filled with a strange euphoria, Freddy convinced Deputy Sheriff Pickup to play cards with him in the back seat.

231

Freddy laughed loudly whenever he won a hand at gin and feigned anger when he lost one. Freddy's behavior made Pickup uncomfortable; it would have been better if Freddy had been quiet and morose for the duration of the long trip.

When Sheriff Carlson stopped for food at a little diner, Freddy ordered a huge meal and ate with great relish. He gulped down several cups of coffee and ordered pie for dessert. He dominated the conversation all during the meal. Because they did not know what to say to a man who had no future, Carlson and Pickup had a hard time engaging in conversation with him. Freddy's death sentence had sequestered him from the ranks of the living. For them, he was a "dead man walking."

During Pickup's turn to drive, Sheriff Carlson sat in back, handcuffed to Freddy, but he wanted nothing to do with him and so kept his conversation to a minimum. It wasn't his job to provide Freddy with entertainment. Eventually, Sheriff Carlson leaned back and closed his eyes. Freddy, ever the little chatterbox, struck up a conversation with Pickup. They drove on into the night towards the town of Ossining.

By noon on Saturday, April 6, Sheriff Carlson was back at the wheel and the two-car convoy crossed over the majestic Hudson River on the Bear Mountain suspension bridge connecting Rockland and Westchester counties. The view from the bridge was spectacular and it was not wasted on Freddy. He soaked up the scenery, recording its details for later recollection in the gray confines of the cell waiting for him at the end of their trip. They were about twenty miles from Sing Sing.

Sheriff Carlson pulled the car up to Sing Sing Correctional Facility at 12:30 p.m. Freddy was escorted through the heavy steel-barred prison gates and was handed over to the Principal Keeper of the prison, John J. Sheehy. When the proper papers were signed, Sheriff Carlson and his deputies exited the prison and headed to a hotel for a well-deserved rest.

Freddy was hustled over to the death house where he was stripped of all his clothing. His naked body was visually inspected from head to toe. He was escorted to a shower stall where he showered under surveillance, then donned a prison gray uniform. Before he was taken to his cell in the east wing of the death house, he was given a pair of prison-made felt shoes. His feet made no noise on the concrete floor as he shuffled down the corridors of the prison.

The death house at Sing Sing was located close to the Hudson River in an isolated corner of the yard, separate from the rest of the prison. It was completely self-sustained, equipped with its own kitchen and hospital. Even the electrical circuit for the electric chair standing in the execution chamber was powered by an alternating dynamo, independent from the main prison. The stories that speak of the dimming of the prison lights when Old Sparky was fired up were untrue.

In 1935, there were thirty-nine cells in the Sing Sing death house. Twenty-four cells, split between east and west wings, held men waiting for their appeals to be heard. Six cells were for men who had lost their appeal and were one step closer to the chair. One of the six inner cells was used as a pre-execution cell. The condemned prisoner was led from a private second door located in the cell, into the hallway known as the "Last Mile." Three cells beyond the east and west wings, separate from the men, were for housing women. There were another six cells set aside for the physically or mentally ill, and three cages for visitation purposes.

Shortly after Freddy was installed in a cell in the east wing, he received a visitor—Lewis Lawes, the man who had sent Freddy to Great Meadow Prison after he participated in the Prison Band strike.

"Well, well, Freddy," said Lawes, who was in the habit of addressing all prisoners by their first names. "We meet again under very different circumstances. I hope you will forgive me when I say I am not pleased to see you again."

"Hello, Warden," Freddy said.

"I have been following your trial in the newspapers. Very sensational, I'd say."

"Yeah, Warden, real sensational, all right."

"You know, Freddy, I wonder from time to time about what became of the men I sent away from here after that strike. I never imagined I would be sending one of them to share a cell with a man he would eventually murder. I hope you don't harbor any resentment towards me for that."

"No, sir, no need to worry about that."

"Well, fine then. Guard, get me a chair, please. Thank you. Now let's have a talk about your stay here, shall we?"

"Yes, sir."

"You will find that life here on death row is very different from the life you spent in a cell block in general population. You have absolutely no privileges here beyond the following: You will receive a haircut twice a month. You will have a five-minute shower every other day. You may eat only in your cell. You may possess a pencil and paper in your cell and nothing else. You may write and receive letters. You may be allowed to save the letters you receive—at our discretion. You may smoke in your cell, but you may not possess matches. The guards will light your cigarettes upon request. You will receive one-half hour in the death row exercise yard everyday if you choose to do so, weather permitting. You may receive visitors, but you will not be granted physical contact with them. In addition, you will remain in this wing until you are either pardoned, had your sentence commuted, or have lost your case with the Court of Appeals. You will be forcibly removed from your cell and placed in solitary confinement if your behavior warrants it. Do you have any questions for me at this time, Freddy?"

"No, Warden. I don't."

"Very well then. I am at your disposal twenty-four hours a day when I am here at the prison. Sometimes my duties as warden require me to travel, so I will not be available to you then. If you need me for anything, you need only ask one of the guards to call me at my office or at my home here on the grounds of the prison. I'll see you again in a few days."

The warden's chair scraped loudly across the shiny concrete floor when he stood and pushed it backwards.

The incoming shift guard walked over to Freddy's cell door and introduced himself. He told Freddy it was okay to call him by his first name. Warden Lawes had found that the men in the death house responded positively to a relaxed set of rules and it helped decrease some of the tension they found themselves under twenty-four hours a day.

Back in Cattaraugus County, Colonel Krieger was standing in the backyard of his home, basking in the afternoon warmth of the April sun. He was watching members of his family play lawn games supervised by his wife. His thoughts drifted back to the reception he received the night before when he arrived home from Little Valley just before eleven o'clock.

A houseful of people was waiting for him. When he entered his house, he received a rousing cheer. The men clapped him on the back and congratulated him on his great victory. The liquor flowed and the household help fed his guests a steady stream of finger-food until the final guest had left at half past two in the morning. For the first time since the discovery of Bernice and Harry Farnsworth's bodies, The Colonel slept well and did not awake until late morning.

Lynn Blessing had gone home when the jury was sent out to deliberate, but Sheriff Carlson called him shortly after Freddy's sentencing to give him the good news. Edith was relieved to hear that the ordeal was finally over. She called up the stairs for her daughter Olive to come down. When Olive appeared, Edith handed her all the photographs of Bernice that had been on display throughout the house.

"Olive," said Edith "be a dear and take these photographs of your Aunt Bernice out of their frames and put them in the family album that you started for me, would you? I don't think we need to be reminded of that tragic incident, don't you agree?"

"Yes, Mother," replied Olive. "How do you want me to caption them?"

"Oh, you needn't write anything beneath them. We all know who she is, now, don't we?"

"As you say, Mother. I'll take care of these tomorrow."

Across town in Salamanca, on Penn Street, Syd Shane arrived home to a quiet house. His wife, Zeita, had already heard the news about Freddy Lindsay's conviction through the grapevine. She hugged her husband when he entered and consoled him over the loss of Freddy's case. Hours later, long after she had gone to bed, Shane sat in the kitchen and chain-smoked over a large pile of notes he had taken over the course of the trial. He was planning Freddy's appeal.

For the next twelve days, Shane met with Mac McCarthy for an hour or two at his office every night around seven o'clock to prepare a Notice of Appeal he intended to file with the Cattaraugus County Clerk. Shane's secretary, Margaret Locklin, finished typing the notice on Thursday, April 17. Shane filed the paperwork in person with Guy Fargo at the County Courthouse on April 18. As a matter of standard procedure, the Court issued a stay of execution until Freddy's appeal was formally filed, which would take place within sixty days and be heard by the Court of Appeals in Albany.

On Saturday, April 20, Shane left Salamanca, bound for Ossining. He arrived at the prison late in the afternoon and visited with Freddy outside one of the visiting cages.

"Freddy! It's good to see you," said Shane. "How are things

here? Are they treating you well?"

"Hi, Syd. It's good to see you, too," Freddy said with true sincerity. "I can't complain about much except the food. And I'm not too happy about being here with a woman on death row. Eva Coo is in a cell above us on the east wing. It's kind of unsettling, you know?"

"No, I didn't know about the woman in death row. I don't keep up on that sort of stuff."

"Yeah, well, I don't like it at all. Did you know that you're the first visitor I've had since I've been here? I was kind of hoping you would be my sister, Helen. She doesn't have the money to pay for a bus ticket. I sure would like to see her one more time."

"Hmmm. I'm sure she'll be able to come soon. Have you been told about your appeal?"

"Yeah. What's going on with that? Warden Lawes told me that my May execution date was cancelled."

"Yes, that's true. Mac and I filed a Notice of Appeal for you last Thursday. The court has automatically granted you a stay of execution. It usually takes several months, maybe more, before the court renders its decision. Mac and I have to put the actual appeal together and that will take a while, too. I feel very confident about the appeal. We have a good chance of getting you a new trial, Freddy. You should never have been tried in Cattaraugus County."

"Okay, Syd. Like I've said before, I trust you guys."

The two men chatted until Shane said he had to leave in order to catch the last train back to Salamanca. He promised Freddy that he would be up to see him when the Court of Appeals rendered its decision. Shane left the prison, caught the train for Salamanca and was home late Sunday evening.

Life went into limbo for Freddy. Meals, showers and time in the exercise yard were the highlights of his day. Every few days one of the guards would plug a small cathedral-style radio into an outlet in the long cell corridor. The inmates would be treated to a Yankees game or a radio show. The inmates loved the radio time because they could escape for few hours from the stress and worry of their impending doom. And the radio temporarily raised a screen of sound between them and Old Sparky, which sat close by, waiting patiently for them.

After working on the appeal for over six weeks, Syd Shane and Mac McCarthy were ready to file their appeal arguments. The Record on Appeal was filed with the Albany Court of Appeals on Thursday, June 6 and recorded as Appeal Number A-1025. Having accomplished that, there was nothing left for Shane and McCarthy to do on Freddy's behalf. So, they sat back and waited. Shane did not expect a response until September or October of 1935.

Freddy's appeal for a new trial was a Statement of Facts, a synopsis of the case, and seven arguments.

The Statement of Facts chronicled events from the time Freddy Lindsay met Harry Farnsworth at Great Meadow Prison, to the murders on March 5, 1935. The last paragraph of the statement laid out the main claim.

"It is the claim of the defendant that the blows which killed Bernice G. Farnsworth were struck by him on sudden impulse when he was acting in self-defense to protect his person from attack from her husband, Harold C. Farnsworth."

The seven arguments covered the denial of the change of venue, denial for a Bill of Particulars for the felony murder in the commission count, the error of the Court in admitting evidence in the killing of Harold Farnsworth, remarks made by the District Attorney and Inspector McDermott concerning Freddy's prison record in violation of his right to a fair trial, Nora Moynihan's testimony in reference to her stolen articles which had served only to incite prejudice among the jury, a verdict contrary to the weight of evidence, and that the defendant was entitled to a new trial based on the previous six points.

Each of the six argumentative points included numerous precedents, lists of newspaper articles, exhibits and excerpts from trial testimony.

Colonel Krieger's response to the appeal was included in the appeal. He chronicled the legal chain of events that occurred from the time the People became involved in the case to the sentencing of the defendant. Then he chronicled the events that occurred on March 8. In two long, argumentative points, he refuted the defendant's claims for a new trial. He cited numerous precedents and quoted many of them extensively. Referring to point three, he stated simply, "The Judgment Should Be Affirmed."

With the filing of the appeal, Syd Shane felt he could finally rest in his fight to save Freddy's life. He packed up Zeita and his son, J. Michael, and left for a two-week vacation at a rented cabin in Quaker Run. When he returned from vacation, he threw himself into his workload. In the back of his head a calendar ticked off the days until September.

On the morning of Thursday, July 11, Syd Shane was reading documents of an interesting lawsuit his office had taken on. He noticed his secretary, Margaret, out of the corner of his eye when she appeared in the doorway to his office.

"Yes, Margaret, I see you. What is it?" he said without looking up.

"We just received some bad news by telephone, boss."

"Oh? What?"

"I received a call from the clerk at the Albany Court of Appeals. They have denied Freddy's Appeal. His new date of execution has been set for the week of August 26."

That got Shane's attention and he shouted, "They what? For Christ's sake, Margaret, that appeal isn't six weeks old yet! What in the Sam Hill is going on here?"

At the same moment, at Sing Sing, Warden Lawes appeared

at Freddy's cell door accompanied by two guards. "Hello, Freddy. How are you today?"

"As good as can be expected, Warden Lawes."

"I'm afraid that I have some bad news for you, son. The Court of Appeals has denied your appeal. I'm here to escort you to the inner cells. That's where all the men go when they have lost their appeal."

Freddy just stood there and Lawes held his breath. Some men lose mental and physical control when they are told such news, others faint. Some men curl up in a fetal position on the floor of their cell and become comatose. Freddy did none of those things. He stood up and faced the cell door.

"I understand, warden. Let's go," he said.

"Thank you, Freddy. I sincerely appreciate your cooperation." Lawes motioned for one of the guards to unlock the door to Freddy's cell. The other condemned men said goodbye to Freddy and called out words of encouragement as he passed by.

When Freddy was safely installed in his new cell, the warden broached the subject of Freddy's new execution date. "You know, Freddy, the Court has set a new date for you, don't you?" he asked cagily.

"Yeah, I kinda figured that, Warden. I was afraid to ask."

"It's been set for the week of August 26. As you know, we schedule executions only on Thursdays here at Sing Sing. So, that puts your date as August 29. Now, don't give up all hope, Freddy. I've seen a lot of men walk out of the inner cells alive. You may be one of them."

"Yeah, thanks. I'll remember that."

After the warden left, Freddy sat on his new bed and figured out the number of days between then and August 29. When he was done he double-checked his calculation. He came to the same total twice. He had six weeks, six days and eleven hours left to live.

CHAPTER SEVENTEEN

As soon as he calmed down after hearing the news about the denial of Freddy Lindsay's appeal, Syd Shane reached for the telephone. He began calling everyone he knew in his circle of influence in Albany, the capital of the State of New York. Eventually, he placed a direct call to the office of the Governor, Herbert H. Lehman. He reached the Governor's secretary and they discussed normal procedures for requests for clemency. Shane had his secretary, Margaret, start on the formal request as soon as he hung up the phone.

On a whim, Shane decided to call Judge Larkin. Surprisingly, the judge was happy to hear from him. They discussed the speed with which Freddy's appeal had been denied. The judge paused and then spoke to Shane frankly and off the record.

"Syd," he began, "you don't understand. Bernice worked with officials in every major law enforcement agency in the State of New York for many years. And I doubt there is a jurist in any of the judicial branches in this state that hasn't dealt with her at one time or another. At the very least, they're familiar with her name. They want justice for one of their own, Syd. And she was a woman who was brutally murdered with an axe. They want to see Lindsay put to death and they will be willing to go to any lengths to accomplish it. You will not find any sympathy for your client from any official. No one is willing to grant clemency for Mr. Lindsay, or a new trial. No one will admit to it, Syd, but believe me, that is what's happening. I was surprised myself with the speed with which the appeal was denied in Albany."

When the phone call ended, Shane put his face in his hands and rested his elbows on his desk. He knew there was truth in what the judge said, but it was not in him to accept defeat easily. Shane made plans to leave for Sing Sing the following Saturday morning. He dreaded making the trip. Shane had nothing to offer Freddy in the way of hope, but he felt he needed to go.

Freddy was moved into the inner cells of the death house shortly after a man named Patrick Downey was transferred to the pre-execution cell that lay fifteen yards from Old Sparky. Downey was put to death at eleven o'clock that evening. Because Freddy himself was physically so much closer to the electric chair, Downey's execution was almost as hard on him as Eva Coo's electrocution had been on June 27. Coo had been convicted of the murder of one of her employees, a slow-witted handyman named Henry Wright. She did it for the insurance money.

Coo killed Wright with a mallet and had another employee, Martha Clift, run Wright over with her car just to make sure he was dead. Martha Clift got a thirteen-year sentence for her part in the crime. Eva Coo received the death penalty.

Whenever women were placed on death row it caused a strange phenomenon in the general prison population. It brought chivalry out from the most hard-boiled criminals incarcerated there. Inmates from the manufacturing shops in the prison would shower condemned women with handmade gifts, given in the hope that it would make their stay on death row easier.

The prison was always placed on lockdown during the rare times a woman was put to death in the chair at Sing Sing. On the day of Eva Coo's execution, Freddy felt as though a thousand ants were crawling over his body. He paced up and down the narrow pathway between his bed and the block wall of his cell. He fought off the urge to grab the bars of his cell door and shake them violently. Every now and then he stifled a scream that rose to the top of his throat. When her execution was over he fell onto his bed, exhausted. It was as if it had been his execution that evening instead of hers.

No one seemed to care that hit man, Leonard Scarnici, followed Coo to the chair minutes after her body had been removed from the death chamber. Just minutes before he was led to the execution chamber, Scarnici confessed to fourteen other murders he committed as a freelance hit man.

Syd Shane arrived at Sing Sing on Saturday, July 13 and visited Freddy. His conversation with Freddy Lindsay was one of the most difficult he had ever had with anyone. He explained that the denial of the appeal was a major setback for Freddy and that there were only two avenues left open. One was clemency from Governor Lehman, the other was a temporary stay of execution in order to re-examine some aspect of Freddy's case. Shane's remarks were followed by an uncomfortable silence. Freddy was the one who broke it.

"Listen, Shane," Freddy began, "I don't know how these things work so I'm going to leave it up to you. Thanks for doing it because I couldn't. In the end, though, I don't think anyone will show me mercy. I killed a woman with an axe. I knew I was done for back then. I hope you don't blame yourself for not getting me off without the death penalty. That would bother me."

"Freddy, there's no need for this kind of talk right now. We've got a good deal of time left. Things could change. Give me some time. Don't give up."

"Yeah, okay. Just don't blame yourself if things don't go well."

Syd Shane returned to Salamanca on Sunday and worked late that night at his office. He worked late every day for the next six weeks. He made countless phone calls and pleaded for help to get Freddy's sentence commuted to life without the possibility of parole. But his pleas landed on deaf or unhelpful ears. Shane was frantic as the days left in Freddy's life were whittling away.

Life in the inner cells at the death house was far different from how it had been in the outer wings. There was nothing for Freddy to do but sit and think or read books that could viewed only when spread out on the floor outside his cell door. He didn't care for the other men caged around him and he kept to himself as a result. His loneliness was agonizing. No one came to visit him.

He spent every waking hour worrying about how much pain he would feel from Old Sparky when it was fired up for him, or else thinking about what he had done to Bernice and Harry Farnsworth.

Although Freddy slept a few hours every night, it was not a restful sleep. Dreams about Old Sparky were replaced with vague, murky ones that took place in the cellar of the McGraw Farm. In this reoccurring dream he struggled to see things clearly until the end of the dream. It always ended with Bernice lying at his feet on the cellar floor in Coldspring.

Freddy wrote letter after letter to his sister, Helen, begging her to come and visit him. His twenty-ninth birthday came and went on August 6 without a visit from her.

Helen wrote back each time and gave him the same excuse for not visiting him. She said she couldn't afford to come. Freddy, in desperation, wrote to Shane asking if he could spare the money for the small bus fare and send it to his sister. Shane dropped a twenty-dollar bill into an envelope with a short note and sent it to Helen as soon as he got Freddy's letter.

Helen received the envelope with the money in it a week before Freddy's execution date. She sat with the letter and the money in her lap. Her only excuse for not visiting Freddy was gone. She prayed she would have the strength to remain calm when she saw him on death row. When her husband, Michael, came home that evening she told him that she had decided to visit her brother on the last day of his life. Michael didn't bat an eyelash. He continued eating his meal and they never discussed the subject again. His silence was all the permission she needed.

The days slipped by and soon there were only two days remaining before Freddy's execution. The guards monitored him closely, looking for signs that he might attempt suicide. Such behavior had been accomplished there on several occasions in the past.

Shane arrived at Sing Sing in the late afternoon of Wednesday, August 28. Warden Lawes was kind enough to put him up at the Warden's Residence on the grounds of the prison. A special telephone line for communication with the Governor's Office was opened in the Warden's Office, just in case news about a commutation or stay of execution for Freddy was received. Shane visited with Freddy on and off until ten o'clock that night. When he retired for the evening sleep did not come.

At six o'clock on Thursday morning, August 29, Warden Lawes walked into the inner cell area and approached Freddy's cell. He advised Freddy that it was time to enter the pre-execution cell.

Freddy was led to the showers, where he scrubbed down, toweled off and dressed in a brand new white shirt, a heavy white diaper, dark trousers and a new pair of felt slippers. Then he was escorted to the death row barbershop where received his last haircut from an inmate barber. Even though hair is a good conductor of electricity, too much of it interferes with the fitting of the metal skullcap on the head of the condemned. Freddy's hair was clipped to accommodate the skullcap. The barber also gave him a good, close shave.

Freddy was escorted to the pre-execution cell and was locked into it. He stared at the heavily barred door that led to the Last Mile and the execution chamber that was just beyond it. Father McCaffrey, the resident Catholic Priest, visited Freddy shortly after he was locked into his cell. Freddy declined to receive any spiritual counseling from him but agreed to his presence in the execution chamber at eleven o'clock that evening.

After all the preparations were over, Freddy lay down on his bed and closed his eyes. His heart pounded thunderously as he thought about his execution. Suddenly, his heart rate slowed and his breathing became normal and relaxed. He was mentally transported back to the McGraw Farm, where he replayed the events of that star-crossed morning, March 5, 1935. He saw himself as he punched Harry in the stomach. Then he saw the struggle between himself and Harry over the axe. And for the first time he saw himself turn and watch Bernice as she rushed across the dirt floor with her gun in her hand. When he saw himself pause and then swing the flat of the axe at Bernice, everything became clear to him. He realized that beyond a shadow of a doubt he had decided to kill Bernice in that brief moment. And he realized that it was not warranted. He accepted full responsibility for his actions. He knew he had killed Bernice Farnsworth with deliberation and premeditation.

When the vision ended with him driving away from the farm in the Sport Coupe, he opened his eyes and sat up in his bed. His fear of death in Old Sparky had evaporated. He understood his death was necessary to bring balance. He had selfishly taken two lives and now he must forfeit his own. It was surprisingly simple, yet profound.

Syd Shane came in to visit him for a while and he told Freddy that they had not heard from Governor Lehman yet. He was still in contact with the governor's office and all the governor's secretary could offer was that the Governor had not made his decision yet. Shane left and went back to the Warden's Office to be near the phone in case a call came in from the Governor.

Freddy spent the next few hours alone. At three o'clock, Helen came in to see him. They were both overwhelmed by emotion but were able to hold themselves together. At first it was difficult to talk because neither of them wanted to speak about his execution. Freddy finally brought up the subject and it broke the ice. Brother and sister talked nonstop for three hours until the Warden came in and told her it was time for her to leave. Their goodbyes were heart wrenching.

Just as Helen prepared to leave she turned and asked, "Freddy, why did you kill those two people? I would have sworn on our mother's grave that you weren't capable of hurting a flea. Why, Freddy? What could they possibly have done to turn you into a murderer?"

Freddy opened his mouth to reply but the words would not come. His pride didn't allow him to admit the selfish reasons for killing Bernice and Harry. He shrugged his shoulders and said nothing. Helen, crying softly, walked out of the pre-execution chamber. She left the prison by taxi. Freddy had less than five hours left to live.

The guard stationed outside Freddy's cell kept him apprised of the time. As with most of the condemned, he constantly asked, 'What time is it now?'

Meanwhile, Robert Elliott, the official executioner, was performing a test run on Old Sparky. When Elliott determined that the chair was performing properly he left for Ossining and had supper at his favorite restaurant.

Freddy chose not to order a special "last meal." When the guard showed up and served the standard prisoner's dinner, which consisted of hamburger, boiled potatoes, lima beans and rice pudding, the other inmates in the inner cells howled. It was customary for the condemned man to order a meal too large for him to eat so that it could be shared with the other condemned men in the inner cells. When Freddy heard their complaints, he shouted back at them and said, "This isn't any goddamn dinner party, you know!"

Syd Shane sat alone in the Warden's office and waited near

the phone. He was an absolute nervous wreck. He chain-smoked and drank many cups of coffee. Whenever the Warden's private phone rang it jangled his nerves so badly he'd jump up from his chair. He prayed silently to God that He might have mercy on Freddy and spare him his life. Warden Lewis Lawes stepped back into his office at ten o'clock. He called the Governor's office at Shane's request.

"Hello," said Lawes into the receiver, "this is Warden Lawes calling from Sing Sing. May I speak with the Governor? It's in regards to Alfred Lindsay. We need to know if the Governor has made his decision about clemency for Lindsay. Have you had any word from him? .... Oh, I see. Is that his final decision? .... All right. Thank you."

Shane's heart dropped to his stomach as he waited for Lawes to divulge the content of his phone call.

"I'm sorry, Syd," said Lawes. "The Governor has denied Freddy's request for clemency and he will not issue a temporary stay of execution. We must move on with Freddy's execution."

Shane collapsed back into the hard wooden chair and let out his breath with a whoosh. Lawes produced a bottle of scotch from his desk drawer and poured Shane an inch and a half of liquid into a glass.

"Here, have this. Believe me, it will help. The worst is yet to come for you. You have to witness his execution."

Shane downed the scotch and it burned its way through his esophagus on its way to his stomach.

At 10:30 p.m., a group of men walked into the Warden's office. They were witnesses seeking approval for access to the execution chamber. Several guards followed them into the room. When the door to the office was closed, Lawes informed everyone that they would be subjected to a thorough search before being admitted to the chamber. Just as the men were removing their suit coats, Deputy Sheriff Leone Pickup entered the room. He was breathing hard, for he had run all the way to the Warden's office.

United States law does not mandate that there be any witnesses to executions, as most people would believe. However, provisions do state that executions have no more than twelve witnesses. Warden Lawes would receive several thousand witness requests from all over the country before each scheduled execution. Lawes generally picked attorneys, judges, lawmen, and one or two newspapermen from the list. In this case, he invited Judge George Larkin and Sheriff Lester Carlson to witness Freddy's execution, with Syd Shane and nine other men. Judge Larkin declined the invitation. Sheriff Carlson also declined the offer, but was able to convince Lawes to allow Deputy Sheriff Leone Pickup to take his place. Pickup had been delayed by bad weather and barely made it to the Warden's office on time.

Pickup introduced himself and asked if he could interview Freddy right away. He wanted an opportunity to clear up a few unanswered questions about the murders.

"Good Lord, no!" exclaimed Lawes. "This man has less than an hour left to live! I won't have him grilled about his crime now. I'm afraid you've arrived too late for that, Deputy Pickup."

Lawes waited as the guards searched each man thoroughly. He had instituted a pre-execution search of all witnesses after the execution of Ruth Snyder in Old Sparky in January 1928. An enterprising reporter from the New York *Daily News* sneaked a camera into the execution chamber by strapping it to his left leg. When the juice was applied to Ruth Snyder, the reporter lifted his pant leg and took a blurry shot as the current from the chair passed through her body. The picture took up the entire front page of the *Daily News* in the next morning's edition. It was the only time anyone ever took a photograph of a condemned prisoner under the full effect of the electric chair.

Lawes lectured the group of men about protocol in the execution chamber and described the process they were about to witness. Shane felt sick to his stomach watching the minute hand click towards eleven o'clock. Lawes left for the pre-execution chamber when he finished with the witnesses.

Lawes and Father John McCaffrey entered the pre-execution chamber at 10:25. Freddy refused Last Rites from the priest, choosing to remain quiet in his cell.

At 10:30 p.m., the witnesses passed through a small vestibule flanked by a coatroom, and entered the chamber through a large, heavy wooden door. They found themselves at the rear of a large and windowless room. The walls were painted stark white and illuminated by overhead lights suspended by rods from the ceiling.

The witnesses were instructed to sit in a row of pew-like benches at the right rear. Syd Shane and Leone Pickup sat next to each another in the first bench. The blocky, angular wooden electric chair was positioned on a large rubber mat in the front center of the room. To the right of the chair was another large wooden door with a black-on-white sign hanging above it. The sign read, "Silence." This was the door by which the condemned entered the execution room.

At the left of the electric chair were two doors. The first led into the autopsy room and the second led into a cubicle that housed the switchboard and the executioner. A white-enameled gurney with thick rubber wheels stood behind the chair. The gurney would be used to transport Freddy's body into the autopsy room after the execution. Autopsies of all executed prisoners were required by law.

The guard who had escorted the witnesses into the chamber pointed at the sign above the door and reminded them that no talking of any sort was permitted in the chamber until the execution was done. He also pointed out the ceramic spittoon that sat at the end of the first bench. Its potential use was obvious.

A few minutes later three guards walked in from the same

rear door the witnesses had used. They walked to the electric chair. They positioned themselves behind and to the sides of it.

At two minutes past eleven, Freddy began his march down the "Last Mile." It was only forty-three steps from his cell door to the electric chair. Father McCaffrey began to read softly from Psalm twenty-three.

"The LORD is my shepherd; I shall not want. He maketh me to lie down in green pastures: he leadeth me beside the still waters...."

The priest began to walk slowly towards the doorway of the pre-execution cell. He was followed by Warden Lawes and Freddy, who was flanked by two guards ready to catch him in case he fainted or went mad.

The priest droned on. "Yea, though I walk through the valley of the shadow of death, I will fear no evil: for thou art with me; thy rod and thy staff they comfort me. Thou preparest a table before me in the presence of mine enemies: thou anointest my head with oil; my cup runneth over...."

The funeral-like procession moved through the execution chamber door and Freddy looked up at the witnesses in the benches to the left of him. He gave Syd Shane a little nod. Shane nodded back. Freddy nodded at Leone Pickup. Pickup sat stone-faced and made no gesture in return.

Freddy looked to the right of the witness area and was stunned by what he saw. Standing in the open area between the witnesses and the far wall were Bernice and Harold Farnsworth. They were dressed in the same clothes they had worn the day they died. Freddy opened his mouth to say something to them but no words came out. Father McCaffrey delivered the last line of the psalm.

"...Surely goodness and mercy shall follow me all the days of my life: and I will dwell in the house of the LORD for ever."

Freddy took step number forty-one as he turned his back to the chair. With steps number forty-two and forty-three, he moved backwards towards the chair and sat down, unassisted. Bernice's eyes filled with tears. Harry's face was crestfallen.

As Freddy continued to stare at the figures of Bernice and Harry standing with their hands clasped together, he attempted to speak to them again. He wanted to say he was sorry. He wanted to say he was wrong. Again, no words emerged from his mouth.

With precision that comes only from experience, the three guards went to work with great speed. The right trouser on Freddy's leg from the knee down was slit open with a razor-sharp penknife. His leg was shaved at the ankle and an electrode with a brine-soaked sponge was attached. His arms, his forearms, chest, lap, thighs, calves and ankles were bound with heavy leather straps. A metal skullcap was fitted over Freddy's head. An electrode that had been dipped into the briny water was inserted into the back of the skullcap. Warden Lawes monitored the whole process as he stood on the rubber mat in front of the chair.

When a leather facemask with two breathing slits for the nose was tied onto Freddy's face, his world went dark. He kept the image of Bernice and Harold in his head. 'I'm sorry,' he said silently to them. 'I'm sorry.' From somewhere very distant Freddy heard the plaintive cry of an eagle.

As soon as the mask was securely in place and the guards were clear of Freddy and the electric chair, Lawes stepped backwards off of the mat. This was the pre-arranged signal for the executioner to throw the switch. The entire process from when Freddy sat down to the time Lawes stepped backward took only forty-five seconds. Robert Elliot threw the first switch and a current of two thousand volts at six amperes raced through the wires attached to Freddy's head and ankle. He never felt a thing. The electricity traveled faster than the body's response to the trauma. It was like receiving a terrific blow to the head. Freddy's brain boiled and the powerful current destroyed his entire central nervous system.

At the instant the switch was thrown, the images of Bernice and Harry shimmered and disappeared.

Freddy's body lurched forward and upward in the chair as the room filled with a faint buzzing caused by the dynamo. Every muscle in Freddy's body contracted to its extreme limit. The visible portions of his face, neck and hands turned crimson. His body swelled to the point where his skin was about to split. Blood spurted from the nose slits in his facemask and it soiled the front of his white shirt. After thirty seconds had elapsed, a wisp of smoke rose from his head. The electrodes, which were capable of heating to almost nineteen hundred degrees, burned through his flesh and helped to fill the room with a sickly, sweet smell. The buzzing of the dynamo was replaced by the sound of frying bacon.

Syd Shane was absolutely sickened by what he saw and heard. He closed his eyes and swallowed the bile that rose in his throat and created a bitter taste in his mouth. The buzzing stopped after a minute and the frying sound tapered off. A young doctor walked up to Freddy and ripped open the front of his bloodstained shirt. Without touching Freddy's body, which was heated to nearly one hundred and thirty-eight degrees, he placed his stethoscope on Freddy's chest and listened to his heart. He stepped back and Robert Elliott threw a second switch that delivered a second charge of electricity through the body for one more minute. Shane did not see the repeat performance but he couldn't help but hear and smell it. Leone Pickup sat and watched the entire process.

When the second charge was cut off, the doctor walked over to Freddy again and probed his chest with the stethoscope in search of a heartbeat. He stepped back from the chair and looked at this watch. He said, "I pronounce this man dead at 11:08 p.m. on August the twenty-ninth, 1935." The execution was over. It had taken less than five minutes to seat, strap and execute Freddy in Old Sparky.

While the guards unstrapped Freddy and gingerly moved his extremely warm body to the gurney behind the chair, Syd Shane bolted from the room. He bypassed the small podium that contained a sheet of paper designed to hold the signatures of each of the twelve witnesses. He had no intention of signing his name to the document. He wanted no record to exist of his participation in the grisly procedure he had just witnessed. He fled the building and waited for the rest of the group at the gate.

Deputy Sheriff Leone Pickup waited his turn to sign the witness sheet and left to find Shane. He found him smoking a cigarette and pacing at the prison gate.

"Well," Pickup said, "what did you think of that?"

"I thought it was the most disgusting thing I have ever seen in my life. That boy did not deserve to die like that!"

"I don't agree with you, Syd," Pickup said. "He got what was coming to him. He murdered my friend Bernice in cold blood with an axe. I don't think he suffered enough for it, but I figure they're pretty much even now. Let's go home, huh? I've had about enough of this prison."

Shane and Pickup left the prison through the huge metal gates and stepped into one of numerous waiting taxis. They did not share a car together on the train trip back to Cattaraugus County.

When Shane arrived home, he swore to his wife Zeita that he would never again take on a capital case. It would be months before Shane could let go of his experience in the execution chamber at Sing Sing.

Helen Short, Freddy's sister, made arrangements to have Freddy's body taken to Beverly Hills Cemetery in Putnam, New York. He was buried in an unmarked grave. Helen was the only person in attendance at the short graveside service performed by a local priest. Helen paid for her bus fare to and from the cemetery with money left over from the twenty-dollar bill Syd Shane had sent her in the mail. She walked away from her brother's grave and never visited it again. She never brought up his name again to anyone. Alfred "Freddy" J. Lindsay was erased from the history of the Lindsay and Short families.

The newspapers in Cattaraugus County ran front-page headlines that announced Freddy's execution in their Friday morning papers. It caused a little buzz over coffee at many kitchen tables, but within a few days it was forgotten. The *Olean Times* described Freddy's two attempts to speak in the execution chamber. The article read:

> As the doomed man entered the chamber his eyes swept over the witnesses sitting in the pews in front of the electric chair. He opened his mouth as if to talk, but seemingly changed his mind. Then his gaze fastened on the guards and physicians standing near the wall to the right of the chair. Again he seemed anxious to say something, but he did not.

Lynn Blessing threw the morning paper into the trash bin in the kitchen and headed out for his photography shop. Edith worried about preparing a new recipe for dinner, and Olive wondered what to wear for her movie date that night. Bobby lay on the divan in the living room, spinning a little red collar around his forefinger and complaining he was bored. Bernice's name was rarely mentioned in the Blessing family again.

Alva Farnsworth read the small blurb in the morning newspaper in Montpelier and sighed. "Maybe things would have been different if I had been able to raise Harry right after the death of his mother," he mused. "Then again," he said with a shrug, "maybe not." He reached for a bottle of forgetfulness and temporarily washed away the memory of his dead son, Harry, by swallowing a big slug of spirits.

Madeline Glossheir, Freddy's old girlfriend in New York

City, stood out on her fire escape looking wistfully down the street in the direction she had watched Freddy approach from the evening he had visited her in March. She held a copy of the morning edition of the *New York Times* in her hand. It was open to the article about Freddy's execution.

Once time had passed, no one in Cattaraugus County remembered much about the legendary murders that occurred in the Murder House on Murder Road. It was a story most people spoke about around a campfire or woodstove. The names and details were forgotten or were incorrect. It remained that way for sixty-five years until a couple from California arrived looking for answers about what had happened to Bernice Kenyon-Farnsworth at her lonely farmhouse in rural Coldspring, New York.

EPILOGUE

THE TWO O'CLOCK SUN SHONE BRIGHTLY ON THE WESTERN-FACING windows of the house on Broad Street in Salamanca, New York. The warmth of its rays heated the old sheer curtains that hung over the windows of one of the bedrooms and filled it with the scent of hot dust. Edith Blessing, seventy years of age, lay in a coma on her bed. She was the victim of several strokes that had taken their toll on her.

Her daughter-in-law, Jeanne Woodruff-Blessing, who was eight-and-a-half-months pregnant, sat in vigil at Edith's bedside. She read a book to pass the time. On the edge of her peripheral vision she detected movement. When Jeanne looked up from her book, she was surprised to find her mother-in-law sitting upright. Edith made eye contact with her. She smiled sweetly and began to speak. "Jeanne, honey, I just wanted to tell you that you're going to have a little girl soon. And don't worry. It's going to be an easy delivery."

Before Jeanne could respond, Edith turned away and fell back onto the bed. Jeanne stood up and shouted for Edith's husband, Lynn Blessing, to come quickly. However, by the time he and Edith's sister, Morna Kenyon, arrived, Edith had slipped completely back into a coma. She did not regain consciousness. Edith died that evening of a cerebral hemorrhage. The date was June 24, 1947.

Two weeks later, almost to the minute of Edith's death, Jeanne gave birth to a little girl at 8:14 on the evening of July 8, 1947. And, as Edith had predicted, it was an easy delivery. Jeanne's husband, Bob Blessing, insisted that the child be named after his late mother. Jeanne, who loved Edith dearly and always called her the perfect mother-in-law, readily agreed. They named their new arrival Sharon Edith Blessing.

~ To be continued: *Coldspring: The Resolution* ~

ABOUT THE AUTHORS

CHERI MANCUSO is a native of Salamanca, New York. She has worked in the field of metaphysics for twenty-seven years, primarily as a psychic medium, a healer, and teacher of metaphysics. Cheri has astounded police and other government-run agencies with her help in the investigation of missing persons, murders, and serial killers. She is particularly eager to help with cases of missing children. Additionally, CEO's and executives of Fortune 15 and 500 companies seek her out for her uncanny accuracy in the world of business. A list of her celebrity clientele reads like a list in *Who's Who*. Cheri has been the subject of many television and radio interviews. She has also appeared in print in national magazines such as *W Magazine* and *LA Confidential*. For more information on Cheri Mancuso, visit **www.mediumcheri.com**.

JOHN SCARANO is the first-generation-American son of Italian immigrants and a native of South Plainfield, New Jersey. He served his country during the Vietnam conflict as an enlisted man with the United States Marine Corps. He has studied metaphysics, tarot, mystical symbolism, and numerology for over forty years and currently teaches private classes on these subjects with his partner, Cheri Mancuso. He is clairsentient, clairaudient and is a Reiki Master. *Coldspring* is the result of John and Cheri's creative and psychic talent. It is their first collaborative publication in which the metaphysical arts were used in character development.